BIOLOGICAL
EDUCATION
IN
AMERICAN
SECONDARY
SCHOOLS
1890-1960

This volume is Number 1 of a Bulletin Series prepared under the auspices of the Biological Sciences Curriculum Study and published by the American Institute of Biological Sciences.

BIOLOGICAL EDUCATION IN AMERICAN SECONDARY SCHOOLS 1890-1960

By Paul DeHart Hurd
Education Consultant
Biological Sciences Curriculum Study
On leave, School of Education
Stanford University

American Institute of Biological Sciences
2000 P Street, N.W.
Washington 6, D.C.

PRINTED IN THE UNITED STATES OF AMERICA

FOREWORD

The Biological Sciences Curriculum Study, with major financial support from the National Science Foundation, is one of the principal educational programs of the American Institute of Biological Sciences. The Curriculum Study, shortly after its organization in January, 1959, established headquarters on the campus of the University of Colorado. The BSCS Steering Committee, under the chairmanship of Dr. Bentley Glass of The Johns Hopkins University, focussed the immediate attention of the Study on the secondary school curriculum in biology.

To facilitate the program involved in preparing new materials for American schools, Dr. Paul DeHart Hurd of Stanford University was invited to make a thorough study—both historical and critical—of the development of secondary school biological education in the United States.

It was apparent that Dr. Hurd's report would be of interest to others besides our committee members. The BSCS Publications Committee, under the chairmanship of Dr. Hiden T. Cox of the American Institute of Biological Sciences, arranged for it to be published as the first number in the *BSCS Bulletin* series. Papers in this *Bulletin* series will appear occasionally and will be concerned with basic developments and problems in science education at all levels with especial reference to the biological sciences. The Editor of the *Bulletin Series* is Francis C. Harwood of the American Institute of Biological Sciences, Washington 6, D.C.

To obtain additional copies of *BSCS Bulletins,* correspondence should be addressed to Mr. Harwood. For information about the BSCS programs, inquiries should be sent to the undersigned.

ARNOLD B. GROBMAN, *Director*
AIBS Biological Sciences
   Curriculum Study
University of Colorado
Boulder, Colorado

February 1, 1961

PREFACE

This study reports the work that has been done on the teaching of biology in the American high school in the period from 1890 to 1961. It is limited to a consideration of curriculum development and investigations of classroom and laboratory learning. Teacher education, professional training of biologists, and special programs for high school students are not considered. The study provides a historical perspective, a digest of research and interpretative summaries about biology teaching that should prove useful to those engaged in the improvement of the high school science curriculum.

It was conducted at the instance of the American Institute of Biological Sciences and with the support of the National Science Foundation. The project was one of the activities of the Biological Sciences Curriculum Study. However, the conclusions reached and the interpretations expressed in this report do not necessarily represent the views of the American Institute of Biological Sciences, the committee members of the Biological Sciences Curriculum Study nor of the National Science Foundation.

I wish to express my appreciation to the staff of the Biological Sciences Curriculum Study and to the AIBS Publications Committee for their contributions to this volume. I am especially indebted to Arnold B. Grobman, director of the AIBS-BSCS, for his counsel and encouragement in the planning and writing of this book.

I also gratefully acknowledge my indebtedness to the colleges, universities and the scientific and professional education organizations for making available unpublished materials on biological education.

PAUL DeHart HURD

CONTENTS

PART I

COMMITTEE REPORTS

I

Introduction

A CONCERN about the nature of science teaching in the high schools has been the cause of much debate in the twentieth century. As science and technology have become distinguishing characteristics of our culture and increasingly important in the solution of the problems basic to our social, economic and political welfare, the nature of an education appropriate for a science-oriented society has become less clear.

The number and complexity of modern scientific theories, the overwhelming growth of new knowledge in every field of science, and the need to develop large resources of technically trained individuals have complicated the problem of modern curriculum development. T. Keith Glennan's (36) comments about the course of scientific development illustrate one aspect of this problem:

> In science, particularly, the tendency more and more has been to penetrate farther and farther into chosen subjects until specialists dig themselves out of sight, and out of hearing, out of understanding of what other scientists are doing in their own and neighboring fields. And, if this state of affairs is alarming, even more alarming is the growing cleavage between science and scientists as a whole and the great mass of humanity in other callings.

The curriculum maker has the responsibility for sifting through the accumulated research in biology to retrieve, by means of certain philosophical criteria, ideas and achievements in a quantity to occupy about 175 hours of instruction—the duration of an average high school course.

Committees of scientists and educators have been at work for over a half century to develop better instruction in science. They have recognized the desirability of courses suitable for the non-specialist, the non-college oriented, the everyday citizen, who finds himself in a world where he cannot escape the need to understand something of the nature of science. They have also seen the problem of providing an added intellectual stimulus in the sciences for those who plan to continue their education beyond high school and who may or may not be considering science as a career. The structure of high school courses—purposes, content and methods—needed to accomplish these ends has been the cause of much educational ferment.

Curriculum problems are persistent and demand a continuous cycle of appraisal, research and development. The cycle in science teaching must be shorter than for most school subjects; the dynamic characteristics of science make this obvious.

Progress in science is closely related to the adequacy of underlying theory. The same may be said for the improvement of education. A first task in curriculum development is a definition of the values of a discipline for a population sample at a particular time and place in the evolution of society. Much has been written about the role of science in our culture and the place it should occupy in the education of young people. The diversity of viewpoints among both scientists and educators about the place of science in a liberal education has had the effect of keeping the secondary school science curriculum static and lagging far behind the modern concepts of science. One is reminded of Aristotle's observation in 300 B.C. after visiting the schools of Athens:

> There are doubts concerning the business of education since all people do not agree on those things which they would have a child taught, both with respect to improvement in virtue and a happy life; nor is it clear whether the object of it should be to improve the reason or rectify the morals. From the present mode of education we cannot determine with certainty to which men incline, whether to instruct a child in which will be useful to him in life, or what tends to virtue, or what is excellent; for all these things have their separate defenders.

A Study of Biological Education

This study reviews the development of biology teaching in the schools of America for the period 1890–1960. It is based upon two kinds of data: 1) the published reports of curriculum committees where the concern was with the improvement of education in secondary school biology, and 2) investigations of curriculum and learning problems in biology teaching.

Committee reports were used to trace the history of modern biology teaching because these statements usually describe the rationale for proposed changes. The criteria used for the selection of particular publications were: 1) the reporting committee was national or regional in scope or was an official committee representing a biological society; 2) curriculum improvement in science was a primary interest of the committee; and 3) the members of the committee were qualified by reason of their background in biological research or teaching experience to justify an opinion on the nature of science teaching. Some committees were composed of representatives from the several sciences taught in high school. The larger committee discussed the problem of science teaching and subcommittees made recommendations for the teaching of the special subjects, such as, biology, physics, or chemistry. The reports ranged in length from a few pages to 600 pages; some dealt with a single problem or issue, such as course content or laboratory work, and others covered the entire spectrum of biological education.

It was decided to discuss the committee reports in a chronological sequence and to group them arbitrarily by ten-year periods with a summary for each decade. There is some logic to this arrangement. The conditions influencing American life and in turn educational practice since 1890 have brought about a series of "crises" in secondary school education. The growth of science and technology has been a major factor although not generally recognized, in creating these tensions. Education in the sciences has never kept pace with the achievements of science, or prepared young people to understand the nature of science and the meaning of scientific progress. Advancements in science and social change reach a point where it is obvious to many that the school science curriculum needs to be assessed and revised. These peaks of concern about the curriculum in schools and the contributing factors become more apparent when the committee reports are presented in the order of their development.

At the risk of over-simplification the events which have in some way influenced education in the sciences for the period covered by this study, 1890–1960, may be described as follows: the closing of the frontier and the beginning of an urban industrial society; the growth of the scientific professions and major contributions to scientific theory, at the turn of the century; the acceleration of scientific and technological developments catalyzed by the first World War; the development of the industrial research laboratory, unknown in 1900; the rise of automation and the economic depression of the thirties; World War II and the birth of the "atomic age"; the engineering and scientific achievements which are symbolized by the "space age"; the systematizing of research and development and the "explosion" in scientific knowledge which are characteristic of the decade, 1950–1960. And, upon entering the Sixties we find that the measure of competitive power in the modern world has become a country's inventory of scientific and technical manpower. In turn and cumulatively these events and others have led to curriculum obsolesence but at the same time suggest directions for redevelopment. Herbert Spencer's essay of 1859 on "What Knowledge is of Most Worth?" poses the question that must be answered with every generation and with every major advance in man's intellectual achievements.

There are other factors which make it necessary to review continually the curriculum pattern in science. Since mid-century we have reached the point where nearly everyone goes to high school. A secondary school education has become the "common school" level to Americans. The growing demand for collegiate education may parallel that for the secondary school. With each rise in enrollment the diversity of the student population becomes accentuated; this in turn places new demands on the science curriculum.

Concepts of what one is to learn from a science course and how one learns this influence not only its content but the way in which the course is organized and presented. Charles Eliot's comment in the *Century Magazine* for June, 1884 is illustrative: "There is very little profit in studying natural science in a book, as if it were grammar or history; for nothing of the peculiar discipline which the proper study of science supplies can be obtained in that way, although some information on scientific subjects may be so acquired." Joseph J. Schwab (78) in the Teacher's Commentary for the experimental biology texts developed by the American Institute of Biological Sciences—Biological Sciences Curriculum Study, 1960, points out that:

> Until very recently, the view was common that science should be represented in the schools mainly or only as a body of useful or interesting truths. Little attention was paid to science as a process of enquiry. Attention to science as a possible vocation was largely limited to two approaches. We tried to rouse interest in the learning and use of information, or we tried to arouse interest in apparatus and techniques. Efforts to lead students to the excitement and satisfaction of problem-solving and of enquiry have been sparse until very recently for we were inhibited by the fact that "coverage" of information was so firmly imbedded as a first priority.

A teacher who believes that a knowledge of biology is indicated by the student's inventory of biological conclusions teaches one way, while the teacher who feels that an understanding of science consists of knowing how knowledge is won and organized presents a different course. Various theories of learning influence the structure of courses as well as the teaching procedures. Good teaching is an activity which will differ under a stimulus-response theory, field theory or a cognitive approach.

Biology is not a course apart in the high school curriculum although it has unique contributions to make to secondary education. Whatever tends to influence education as a whole has implications for biology teaching. It is within this complex of scientific developments combined with social, psychological, and educational forces that the science curriculum exists. This is also the framework within which each science curriculum committee works.

Whatever the biology curriculum developed there are always questions about its learning values and the best means for conducting class and laboratory work. In the second part of this study there is a classified review of much of the reported research on the teaching of biology. Investigations or surveys of only local interest have been omitted. Research on teacher and special education in biology were not a part of this study. There are many investigations on biology teaching that have not been published, efforts were made to secure the loan of these studies and with some success.

This study in its entirety attempts to summarize and relate the work that has been done on biological teaching in America. There are unexplored areas and gaps both in philosophy and research that suggest the need for a continuing study of biological education.

II

Biological Education, 1890–1900

IN THE PERIOD between 1890 and 1900 American secondary education underwent serious questioning relative to its proper function and purpose. Increasing enrollments and a diversity of interests of pupils entering high school forced high school administrators to consider a broader curriculum than one centered exclusively on college preparation. Previous to 1890 nearly everyone that graduated from high school continued his education in a college or university. The percent of the school population 14 to 17 years of age completing high school, however, was extremely small since only 3.8 percent of this age group was enrolled in school. Between 1890 and 1900 the number of high schools increased from 2,536 to 6,005 and the percent of young people in high school increased to 8.4 percent of the 14-17 age group. The enrollment of girls exceeded that of boys by about 25 percent.

With the onset of industrialization and urbanization the demands for a high school education increased but the percent of students aspiring to a college education decreased. While the number of students in colleges rose during this time the enrollment represented a decreasing fraction of the high school population.

Nearly all of the students graduating from high school between 1890 and 1900 had had a course in physics and about half had taken chemistry. Physiology was taken by 28 percent of the pupils; exact data do not exist for the enrollments in the other biological sciences which were much smaller than in physiology. Course offerings in biology were extensive. A survey of the high schools in New York State for the period 1896–1900 showed that 82.5 percent of the schools taught botany, 70 percent physiology, 42.5 percent zoology, and 10 percent biology. Science offerings and enrollments changed radically in the twentieth century.

9

A new era in secondary education and high school biology teaching opened in 1893 with the report of the National Education Association's *Committee on Secondary School Studies,* also known as the Committee of Ten (60). Charles W. Eliot, President of Harvard University and a former professor of chemistry at the Massachusetts Institute of Technology, had been the general chairman for this committee. Its function was to investigate the whole field of secondary education as conducted in private academies and public high schools. Subcommittees on natural history, botany, zoology and physiology were established to study the teaching of these subjects in grades one through twelve.

The *Committee on Natural History* agreed that botany and zoology ought to be introduced in the first grade and pursued steadily with not less than two periods a week throughout the elementary school. It was suggested that textbooks not be used in the early grades. A course in nature study for the eight years of the elementary school was outlined.

The *Botany Committee* recommended a high school course on the study of typical plants as an introduction to plant development, but cautioned that the work should not be confined to isolated and hence barren facts. Frequent lectures were to be given to broaden the outlook of the student. The suggested organization of the course was three laboratory periods, one lecture and one quiz a week. In the study of each plant the work should include cell structure, development, reproduction, and life history accompanied by drawings and verbal descriptions to stimulate close observation.

The committee recommended the following year course in botany:

First semester:
1. Green slimes, oscillatoria
2. Green algae, protococcus, spirogyra, diatoms
3. Brown algae, fucus
4. Red algae
5. Fungi
6. Stone worts, nitella

7. Bryophytes, liverworts and a moss
8. The pteridophytes and perhaps a club moss
9. A gymnosperm
10. The phanerogams, trillium and capsella
Second semester:
  1. Plant structure
  2. Physiology
  3. Classification of plants

The *Zoology Committee* recommended a forty-week course of five hours per week. Of the 200 hours, 120 should be in a laboratory study, and 80 hours in reports on laboratory and textbook work. It was suggested that the course begin with a study of a single animal, such as the goldfish, to be studied in its entirety as a living organism. A brief textbook for the course would be advisable but not entirely important. The outline of a year's course in zoology was given as follows:

1. Protozoa
2. Porifera
3. Coelenterata
4. Echinodermata
5. Vermes
6. Mollusca
7. Arthropods
8. Insects; use the grasshopper as a type insect followed by the study of six or eight orders and conclude with having each student make a crude classification of insects.
9. Study of the vertebrates:
   a. fish
   b. frogs
   c. reptiles
   d. birds
   e. mammals, with some orientation toward man

In teaching zoology it was suggested that students examine the external anatomy of animals, study the general form, regional parts and symmetry. Following this, there should be a "comparison with other individuals of the same species, emphasizing points of variation and constancy and comparison with other types." Observations of living animals, simple physiological tests and the drawing of inferences from their reactions were recommended. "Class topics and talks by the teacher" would be used when the class was not involved in laboratory work. The committee decried the dependency of zoology teaching on textbooks and the learning *about* animals. It felt laboratory work would do much to correct these conditions particularly if "quality work" was emphasized.

Both the botany and zoology committees agreed that it was absolutely necessary to have laboratory work and laboratory notebooks in biology so that students could learn to express themselves clearly and exactly in words or by drawings. They also agreed that both a written and a laboratory test should be required in all science examinations and that the laboratory notebooks of pupils should be presented for examination at the time of the test.

The *Committee on Physiology* in the primary and secondary schools recommended that the principles of hygiene should be taught in the lower grades and physiology as a science should be placed in the upper years of the high school. A one-semester course in each of anatomy, physiology and hygiene was recommended, with an emphasis upon practical work, stressing the mechanics, physics and chemistry of the body. The committee was careful to note that "while physiology is one of the biological sciences it should be clearly recognized that it is not like botany or zoology, a science of observation and description, but rather like physics and chemistry, a science of experiment." However, because of the limitations on experimental work in physiology in high school a historical study of the organs of the body was suggested. Furthermore, teachers were to make suitable use of practical exercises, demonstrations and working models wherever possible. Hygiene, if it had not been covered in the elementary school, should be directed toward dietetics, heating, ventilation, water supply and drainage.

The *Committee of Ten* recognized that the secondary schools in the United States, taken as a whole, do not exist for the purpose of preparing boys and girls for colleges. Only an insignificant percentage of the graduates of high schools continue study in colleges or scientific schools. A secondary school science curriculum intended for national use must, therefore, be made for those pupils whose formal education terminates with the high school. The "feeble" and "scrappy" nature of the typical secondary school program, the lack of highly trained science teachers and the improper placement of subjects in the curriculum sequence also caused concern.

After a series of sessions the committee concluded its meetings with the following resolution on the science program for high schools:

> ... at least one fourth of the time of the high schools should be devoted to nature studies, and that this amount of preparation should be a requirement for entrance to college.

In 1896 the Department of Natural Science Instruction of the National Education Association was "organized by the scientific men of the country." Charles E. Bessey, as president, took the opportunity to raise some questions about the place of high school science in our culture (12). His comments on the "new education," in which science was to have a prominent part in the high school, were focused upon the purposes of the science courses. He questioned whether the science taught should be only "useful" and of an "applied" nature, or should some effort be made in a "cultural direction"; should not science be something more than accumulating facts, with more attention given to the classification, arrangement and the generalization from facts—the development of a 'judicial state of mind'? The recorder for this meeting states there was much discussion on "science as a framework for future achievement."

A science committee, under the chairmanship of E. H. Hall (37) of Harvard and sponsored by the National Education Association, issued a statement in 1898 reacting to the reports of the science committees established by the *Committee of Ten*. The following recommendations were made: 1) all science courses in high school should be two semesters in length; 2) they should have the same weight for college admission as other courses; 3) all laboratory periods should be two hours long; 4) there should be four hours of laboratory work per week and two periods of recitation and demonstration; and 5) colleges and universities should require science for admission.

The committee's reaction to the teaching of high school science was that 1) courses "should be designed in the interest of the school pupil, without reference to whether the pupil will enter college or not. The college must fit itself to the high school . . . . and adapt courses so as to offer a suitable continuation of the preparatory course for the benefit of those students who enter with credit in the subject." 2) "the minute anatomy of plants or animals, or specialized work of any kind, is premature and out of place in a high school course of one year in length." 3) The high school work should confine itself to the elements of the subject . . . full illustration of principles, and methods of thought . . ."

John M. Coulter, chairman of the *Subcommittee on Botany in Secondary Schools,* criticized severely the common practice of examination and recitation on the gross structure of flowering plants accompanied by herbarium observations as being "superficial and restricted and even an irrelevant presentation of biological science . . ." Coulter recommended the "new method" using the "compound microscope and examination of minute structures of representative plants" as more appropriate for high school use.

An ecological approach to the teaching of botany providing an over-all picture was proposed. A one-semester course was recommended to include: 1) life relations, a study of vegetative and reproductive organs; 2) plant groups, not a full study but introductory; and 3) plant societies.

The inadequate preparation of students entering college before the turn of the century was a matter of deep concern on the part of college faculties. The National Education Association in

1895, appointed a committee of twelve university scientists and an equal number of high school teachers to consider college entrance standards (63). Specifically this committee was charged to harmonize relations between the secondary schools and the colleges. Its goal was to seek ways in which the former could do their legitimate work as schools of the people and at the same time furnish adequate preparation to pupils intending to continue in the academic colleges and technical schools.

When the committee reported in 1899 they recommended that the study of nature be an integral part of school work preceding the high school. For the second year of high school one of the following course organizations was proposed: biology, botany, or zoology; or a semester each of botany and zoology. Each course should be allowed one unit of credit toward college entrance requirements. These courses, including a large amount of individual laboratory work supplemented by field work, were to be taught not less than four periods per week. The pupil should be required to make careful drawings and descriptions in a permanent notebook. Such laboratory work, including the notebook, should occupy one-half of the assignments. The committee felt that good laboratory work required double periods.

A subcommittee on the teaching of botany recommended that the course include instruction by textbook, informal lectures, and frequent quizzes, elucidating and enforcing the laboratory work so that the pupil would gain a comprehensive and connected view of biological principles, rather than merely a knowledge of a few disconnected facts. It was also recommended that the entire course consist of plants as living things at work, details of structure being entirely subordinated. Professional terminology, complicated and expensive apparatus were to be avoided as much as possible. The teacher should insist upon constant and accurate drawings to secure precise observations. Care should be taken, however, not to overload the student with details or to demand too exhaustive a study of single forms. Classification should be on a rational basis with a consideration of the entire plant kingdom. The first contact with plants should be general and in reference to the physical and biological environments. At least a half-year of botany should be devoted to a study of general morphology, including:

1. The great plant groups
2. Life relations and processes
3. Plant societies
4. Plant structures

Colleges and universities were advised to establish a suitable advanced course for entering students who had completed the requirement in botany and in no case should these students be placed in the same class with beginners.

The subcommittee on zoology recommended that botany and zoology be studied in successive terms or years because of their similarity. There was unanimous opposition to the textbook method of teaching zoology in the high schools where "a large amount of information about animals is acquired thereby in a limited time, and a minimum of attainment and preparation is demanded of the teacher." The use of the taxonomic approach in high schools was discouraged since it gives the student an exaggerated notion of the importance of structural parts for a limited group of animals and fails to develop biological ideas. The study of zoology should be limited to a few types with an "emphasis on the quality of the work rather than the amount of ground covered." For the most part the committee thought that external morphology, life history, habits and the economic importance of animals were of far greater interest and value to high school pupils than the systematic and morphological approach typical of colleges. It was recommended that five hours per week should be spent in the study of zoology, two hours for classroom work and three in the laboratory.

The *Committee on College Entrance Requirements* made the following recommendations for the placement of science subjects in schools:

Elementary School —Nature study, at least two exercises
(Grades 1–8) per week

High School—Grade 9—Physical geography
　　　　　　　Grade 10—Biology; botany and zoology; or bot-
　　　　　　　　　any or zoology
　　　　　　Grade 11—Physics
　　　　　　Grade 12—Chemistry

All courses were to meet at least four periods per week and carry one unit of college entrance credit. One year of high school science was recommended as a requirement for all students entering college.

Programs for the gifted students in high school were considered. It was proposed that gifted students be allowed to complete preparatory science courses in less time and that credit toward a degree be granted when the high school work was equivalent to college work. Credit for a second year of work in one science was recommended; this would allow the student to receive credit for both a year of botany and a year of zoology. An increase in the length of the school day with more study in school under supervision was also suggested.

Summary, 1890–1900

The decade from 1890–1900 was a period of concern about both secondary education and the nature of education in the sciences. More young people were continuing their education into high school and college. College faculties were disturbed by the lack of uniformity in training and the quality of learning possessed by entering students.

A consensus of the committee reports on the improvement of biology teaching shows:

1. The desirability of a continuous offering of biological science from the first grade through high school.
2. The establishment of a required course in biological science at the tenth-grade level.
3. The requirement of one year of biology for entrance into college.
4. The need for more uniformity of content in high school biology.

5. The teaching of biology as a laboratory science.
6. The need for an emphasis in biology teaching on the broader principles of the discipline.
7. The importance for all young people to receive instruction in hygiene and human physiology before completing high school.

The decade from 1890–1900 has been characterized by G. W. Hunter as the great period of the laboratory manual in biology teaching. The growth of laboratory work received its strongest support from the "mental discipline" theory of psychological development rather than from any biological justification. Laboratory work in all the sciences was seen as an ideal procedure for the training and exercising of these faculties of the mind devoted to observation, will power and memory. This theory of learning was rejected by psychologists soon after the turn of the century. As late as 1960 the excuse for biology laboratory work in a surprising number of secondary school curriculum studies and textbooks is still that of "mental discipline."

A distinguishing characteristic of the 1890–1900 period in biological education was a shift away from a natural history approach to courses of "pure" botany and zoology with the major emphasis upon morphology.

It cannot be assumed that either teaching practices or the structure of biology courses immediately reflected the recommendations of the curriculum committees for any period reported in this study. Nor is it possible to state at any particular time whether the work of an earlier committee had widespread acceptance among classroom teachers. Over a period of a half century one can recognize that a gradual change has taken place in the content and manner of biology teaching, although the observation of a number of individual courses in the schools of today would reveal examples of every decade herein reported.

III

The Beginning of General Biology, 1900–1910

ALTHOUGH A FEW high school courses were taught under the title of biology before 1900 they were not organized around a biological theme nor did they present an integrated "picture" of the biological sciences. In the period from 1900–1910 various local and national committees gave thought to a unified biology course. The rapid growth in the secondary school population of pupils who had no intention of continuing to college, stimulated curriculum makers and classroom teachers to experiment with courses in *applied* or *practical* biology. It was assumed that biology for the citizen and biology for the potential specialist should be different in character and content.

In 1905 the *Biology Committee of the Central Association of Science and Mathematics Teachers* presented the following recommendations for the teaching of high school biology (72):

1. There should be a full year of botany or zoology rather than a half year of each subject.
2. The work in biology should be preceded by an "elementary science" to familiarize the student with laboratory methods and to provide a basic knowledge of chemistry and physics.
3. The course should meet six periods per week with double periods for laboratory or field work.
4. Botany and zoology should be acceptable to colleges as entrance requirements.

More field work was strongly recommended in addition to "a plot of ground for growing things." A better balanced program of biology was suggested with a fair proportion of attention given to morphology, physiology, ecology and economics. The committee felt that biology courses should start "at the most accessible point," and that a "simple to complex" sequence was not essentially the best approach for high school students.

The *New York Board of Regents* developed a course in general biology as early as 1899. The course was in reality a series of sub-courses in botany, zoology and physiology offered in a one-year period. George W. Hunter, then a New York City high school biology teacher, in 1907 published a textbook called *Elements of Biology* which attempted to "place the topics required or suggested by the Regents' syllabus into a connected form." (41)

In 1909 the *High School Teachers Association of New York City* issued a report on "The Practical Use of Biology" (51). It was noted that the teaching of biology was going through a period of radical transformation with increasing emphasis upon "training in living" and upon "the practical use of the subject." The committee supported this point of view and made the following specific suggestions for the improvement of course content in biology:

1. *An economic phase*—the preserving of natural resources.
2. *A health phase*—the relation of foods to efficient work of the animal body; the importance of pure foods and safe medicine; the cause and prevention of disease; the proper regulation of personal habits.
3. *A cultural phase*—development of an intellectual stimulus for a sympathetic interest in nature and the interrelationship of man and other beings; the proper conception of man's environment is a rare possession and this acquisition should be striven for.
4. *A disciplinary phase*—the habit of accurate thinking is a serious need in civilized life, and biology offers the data and method for making training of this kind effective; the only important mental discipline is that which is effective when applied to the problems of everyday life.

The *American Society of Zoologists* in 1906 made recommendations for improving the teaching of zoology in the high schools (13). The Society was of the opinion that ". . . zoology should have a place in general education" and should be studied in high school since so many students do not continue into college. The Society recommended that a full year of zoology be taken by the student if the course was to be offered for college credit, or one-half credit in zoology and one-half credit in botany to make a full year's work in biological science for those not using the course for college admission. The development of an advanced course in zoology in the high schools was opposed on the basis that it would of necessity be too specialized.

The proposed course outline for a year's work in high school zoology was:

1. *Natural history,* structure in relation to adaptations, life histories, geographical range, relations of plants to animals and economic relations.
2. *Classification of animals* into phyla and leading classes and prominent orders in cases of insects and vertebrates.
3. *General plan of external and internal structure* for the following animals: one vertebrate (fish or frog) in comparison with the human body; an arthropod, an annelid, a coelenterate, and a protozoon.
4. *General physiology* of above types, and comparisons with human physiology and with the life processes in plants.
5. *Reproduction* of the "protozoon, hydroids, and the embryological development of the fish or frog."
6. *Evidence of relationship*—"suggesting evolution," and a few facts on adaptation and variation, "but the factors of evolution and the discussion of its theories should not be attempted."
7. *Optional*—Some epoch-making discoveries of biological history and the careers of eminent naturalists.

The Society stressed the need for laboratory facilities and a good textbook. Two-thirds of the course should consist of laboratory and notebook work, the notebook to be submitted at examination time with carefully labeled drawings of the chief anatomical structures studied.

In 1906, E. G. Dexter studied the impact of the report of the

Committee of Ten (1893) on the teaching of biology in high schools (29). He examined 80 courses of study in biology published before 1895 and 160 courses of study used by schools in 1905. He found, contrary to the *Committee of Ten*'s recommendations, that physiology courses in high school had decreased fifty percent and that attempts were being made to teach it in the lower grades. Furthermore, that while more high schools were teaching botany and zoology, the courses were not being offered for a full year as had been recommended. He also found that biology teachers reacted against the morphological approach suggested as desirable by the *Committee of Ten*.

Dexter felt that little was achieved by the *Committee of Ten* in actual practice, even though their report was 1) the center of many educational discussions; 2) the members of the committee were widely recognized in scientific circles; 3) the committee membership was larger than any previous committee in the history of education; and 4) the report had been well advertised and had had the widest reading.

H. R. Linville, reflecting on the teaching of biology in the high schools from 1890–1900, made this observation (52):

> The teachers of morphological biology in the schools brought with them from the colleges certain ideas of method. Possibly the lecture system never took strong hold in the schools, but the laboratory method of the college with much of its paraphernalia, did. The consequence of this was that thousands of young and untrained pupils were required to cut, section, examine, and draw the parts of dead bodies of unknown and unheard of animals and plants and later to reproduce in examination what they remembered of the facts they had seen.

The decline in enrollments in human physiology, the general dislike of the course by students and the difficulties experienced in teaching it were popular topics of discussion at association meetings of science teachers between 1900–1910. Oscar Riddle in 1906 suggested that human physiology be made a part of the zoology course with an emphasis on physiology rather than morphology (75). He felt that the course should be made suitable for the ninety percent of the high school students who did not go on to college.

C. Crosby in 1907 reported on several surveys he had made on the teaching of human physiology in the high schools (26). He found a strong negative feeling in students about physiology courses. His study revealed that practically all the laboratory work on human physiology was with lower organisms or of a chemical nature. Most of the students took the course before they had had zoology or botany and therefore had little background for the type of work being taught. He recommended the development of a zoology course organized in a sequence from lower animals through man and unified by a theme of physiology.

In 1907, the *Central Association of Science and Mathematics Teachers* appointed a committee "to prepare a statement of a biological creed that might serve as a guide in the development of biology courses." The committee published its deliberations in March, 1909 (16).

It was assumed at the outset that it would be undesirable if biology courses in all localities were the same. The major differences in teaching high school biology were found to arise from unequal knowledge about the subject, the goals to be sought, materials and procedures to be used in obtaining the desired ends, the relative importance of the various phases of the subject and the point of departure.

The committee thought that biological subjects were peculiarly fitted for general education purposes because of the "light they throw on the study of life." For instance through the study of plants and animals a knowledge of life processes may be gained from which the student can derive an interpretation of his own place in nature. Accordingly, biology courses in high school were seen as having both general and cultural values for *all* students.

Accurate, dependable and efficient methods of thinking were to be sought in biology teaching because of the excellent opportunities for students to utilize their knowledge in solving problems. A firsthand knowledge of "cause and effect" should be a focus in every course in the biological sciences. The practical use of biology as it is applied to the fields of forestry and agriculture is not to be overlooked, nor are the lifelong pleasures to be derived from a knowledge of biology. Questions about the relative importance of morphology, physiology, and ecology were not considered to be issues if the course was a study of living organisms.

The committee suggested that methods of teaching should be related to the student's previous experience, or at least not totally unrelated. The work on nutrition and reproduction should be prominent and might best serve as a "take-off point" for the study of most organisms. Course work should be based on firsthand experience, with each assignment looked upon as a problem to be solved. Sufficient time must then be allowed for its solution. Textbook, lecture and illustrative work would follow the study of a problem and be based upon the student's experience with it. Experiments should in many cases precede the reading of the text and the hearing of lectures.

It was felt by the committee that there should be a balanced picture of the realms of biology rather than specialized courses in botany, zoology, and physiology.

In 1908, the editors of *School Science and Mathematics* requested a number of university biologists who had given attention to the educational as well as the academic aspects of the subject to comment upon the following questions (82):

1. "What is the purpose of biology in education?"
2. "What are the practical, pedagogical, and scientific bases for the study of biology in secondary schools?"
3. "Should the study of biology be a single science, a series of sub-courses in botany, zoology and human physiology or separate courses?"
4. "Should there be more attention to the economic and industrial aspects of the material included?"

A consensus was apparent on several of the questions:

1. The course in biological science should be "adapted to the majority of pupils."
2. The course should stress general education values in terms

of being practical and in the broadening of pupil interests and the deepening of appreciations.

3. Biology courses should be focused more on the ideas and principles of the discipline.

The greatest diversity of feeling occurred on how biology courses in high school should be organized: 1) as a single course without sharp distinction between botany, zoology and human physiology; 2) "sub-courses" in each of these fields for one third of the year; or 3) a year's work in each field.

The *Central Association of Science and Mathematics Teachers* in 1910 issued a committee report described as taking "stock of our philosophy of using the sciences and mathematics as a means of education" (34). The committee agreed that the general purposes of high school education must always be allowed to condition the special purposes of the sciences.

The major problems of science teaching in high school were seen as motivation of students, selection of teaching materials, and teaching "the scientific spirit and method" as opposed to arbitrary methods. "It is not enough merely to secure the pupils' assent to a fact, or to an observation properly made and recorded, or to memorize a set of words or relations . . . even if correct."

The following problems on the teaching of biology were identified:

1. Failure to use student experiences
2. The appropriate degree of "rigor" in the content of the course
3. Limitations of the laboratory
4. Tendency to cover too much material

The committee observed that:

"The present period is one of protest against methods and matter; a period of dissatisfaction and retesting the curriculum; a period of study of the grounds and history of teaching."

Their suggestions for the improvement of biology courses were:

1. More emphasis on "reasoning out" rather than memorization.

2. More attention to developing a "problem-solving attitude" and a "problem-raising attitude" on the part of students.

3. More applications of the subject to the everyday life of the pupil and the community, and "this does not mean a commercialization or industrialization of science . . . although these are practical phases of this life value."

4. More emphasis on the incompleteness of the subject and glimpses into the great questions yet to be solved by investigators.

5. Less coverage of territory; the course should progress no faster than pupils can go with understanding.

The strength of the biology course was that it naturally allows a good adjustment "to the life needs of the pupil." "Its best appeal is in its appeal to the habit of discriminating among the numerous factors that enter into results; in its emphasis on the great unifying and progressive phenomena of all life; in its encouragement to openness of mind—its shibboleth being 'evidence' rather than 'proof'; and in its parallelism with human interests."

"Botany and zoology should be so handled that human physiology and hygiene and the elements of anthropology will naturally become the culmination of the course. While human interest in plants and animals should fill a large place in this course, human interest means much more than commercial or economic interest." Biology "should be a progressive and spiral intermingling of the ecological, physiological, systematic and economic phases of the subject." The course should be supplemented with a "well-selected calendar study of plants and animals running through the entire school year . . ."

"Among the great principles to which the student should be led are: growth and progressive development, both individual and racial; division of labor and differentiation for efficiency; sexual differentiation and its meaning; the economic dependence of man on other organisms; the value of social combination and service; and the natural processes of the human mind itself in passing from observations to conclusions."

The committee suggested that one half year of biology be offered in the ninth grade, and that a year course be required in the tenth grade, with elective courses in grades eleven and twelve.

Summary 1900–1910

In the decade from 1900–1910 the high school course in "biology" had its birth. By 1910, however, only 1.1 percent of all high school students were enrolled in the course. The separate subjects of botany, zoology and physiology were beginning to lose enrollment both from the lack of pupil interest and inroads of the new course. The "new" biology course, although it was established to present a unification of botany, human physiology and zoology, was actually three sub-courses combined in a one-year sequence.

The decline of the special biological sciences was both heralded and condemned. Some writers felt a combination course would force biology teachers to focus on the important ideas about living things, and others thought that a course of this nature could be only superficial. Typical of the first point of view was a statement by C. W. Hargitt (38):

> I plead for biology in the schools—biology rather than botany or zoology, whether singly or in successive courses. Biology means more than either alone, is more than either. It deals with organisms as being, acting, interacting; sensitive, irritable, responsive and adaptive to a degree seldom realized by those untrained to observe. Its subjects live, struggle, thrive, achieve, or they suffer, decline, and perish.

Conversely W. F. Ganong, whose book on the teaching of botany had been standard for two decades, commented upon the new course as follows (35):

> In some places the Botany and Zoology are combined into a single year of Biology, with no additional instruction in those subjects. This method has the serious demerit of yielding a very defective knowledge content for both sciences. In any subject

there is a point up to which, while the training is all valuable, the knowledge acquired is relatively small; and it is, I believe, the common experience that knowledge in these sciences follows in proportionally greater amount in the latter part of the year. I think, therefore, that a full year of either Botany or Zoology, is of much more value than the combination half year of each. In some cases where the course in Biology is used, provision is made for a full elective year later in either Botany or Zoology, and such a plan fully meets this objection.

Some of the significant developments in biology teaching during the 1900–1910 decade were:

1. A growing commitment to a single course of general biology in the high school, integrating materials from botany, zoology and human physiology.
2. An awareness of the "average" student who will not continue into college and the desirability of developing for him a more practical (applied or economic) type of biology course.
3. The appearance of the first high school textbooks on *biology* intended to replace the separate texts of botany, zoology and human physiology.
4. The attempt to orient biology teaching toward biological principles, ideas and interrelationships.
5. More emphasis was given to the "scientific method" and the "practical" objectives for biology teaching.
6. The breakdown of the "mental discipline" theory in learning with more importance attached to capitalizing on student interests and experience.
7. The failure of human physiology to become established as a separate course in the curriculum; the enrollment in the course dropped almost 50 per cent between 1900 and 1910.

The popular writings of the period contained numerous disparaging remarks on the "fern-fish", and "the bale of hay and pail of frogs" types of biology courses. Mostly the comments were criticisms of a teaching practice consisting of name-observe-compare-dissect-draw-label-memorize-test routine with non-living organisms the object of attention. Oscar Riddle's comments are typical: "And what objects do our students handle and how do they handle them? I answer that in the majority of laboratories they use dead unyielding specimens which have centralized within themselves all the rigidity that is within the power of over-proof spirits to impart" (75).

IV

The Changing Science Curriculum, 1910–1920

THE PERIOD from 1910–1920 in American history was one of great industrial expansion. It was during this time that many Americans began to develop some awareness of the importance of science although with a limited meaning. At the same time, a decreasing fraction of the high school population was graduating with credits in the physical sciences. Botany, zoology and physiology continued to drop in enrollment. On the other hand, general biology was becoming increasingly popular with high school students. It represented the first science course in the secondary school curriculum to be planned for the majority of students.

A major development in the science curriculum between 1910 and 1920 was the introduction of general science into the ninth grade. The typical offering at this level had been a semester of physiology and a semester of physiography. The physiology course was proving to be unsatisfactory and biology teachers wanted more physical science as a background for tenth grade biology. The first courses in general science were a compendia of several sciences: physiology-hygiene, physiography, astronomy, geology, meteorology, chemistry, physics, botany and zoology. It was expected that the course would provide a more adequate preparation for tenth grade biology and an orientation to all the science offerings in the high school. It was also a hope that students taking general science would be stimulated to elect further courses in science.

The course content of general science was concentrated in the physical sciences. Whatever was given in the biological fields was usually repeated in the biology course, a duplication that still persists.

Several significant committee reports were developed during

the 1910–1920 period. The first was that of the *Committee of Nine on the Articulation of High School and College* (43) of the National Education Association in 1911. A recommendation was made that high schools require every student to complete two subject majors of three credits each and one minor of two credits. Science was designated as one of the possible majors. The committee proposed that one year of science be a requirement in high school and recognized that this would most frequently be biology. This recommendation further established science as a part of the secondary school curriculum and strengthened the position of biology.

In 1912 the *Central Association of Science and Mathematics Teachers* (17) appointed a committee to study "the need for better unification in aims and practices in science teaching, and a better unification in the content of the science courses of the different years of the high school." Its recommendations were reported in 1914. The chairman, Otis W. Caldwell, stated that even after several years of discussion all members of the committee did not concur on the following recommendations:

A. The purposes of science instruction are:
   1. To provide a knowledge of the world of nature as it relates to everyday life.
   2. To stimulate pupils to direct and purposeful activity leading to more intelligent choice of future studies and occupations.
   3. To provide methods of obtaining accurate knowledge which should be useful in helping pupils solve their own problems and to develop an abiding belief in the value of accurate knowledge.
   4. To help develop a greater and clearer knowledge of nature and thus lead toward better understanding and, consequently, enjoyment of life.
B. The course of study in science should include:
   1. *First year,* "a broad basis involving fundamental principles of the various sciences and using materials from all, if needed." It is to be preferred that certain large topics be studied in place of many small topics.
   2. *Second year,* a course in the fundamentals of various sciences

with an emphasis upon the biological sciences and their applications interwoven with commercial and physical geography. The second year course should build upon the first and also introduce many principles of physics and chemistry.
3. *Third and fourth years,* courses along the lines of physics and chemistry with other opportunities for electing a science such as agriculture or home economics.

The first two years of science were to be required and serve as a basis for a program continuing into physics or chemistry or into the special science offerings. It was suggested that courses in physiology and hygiene offered in the ninth grade be removed from the science curriculum and placed in the department of physical education.

The *Committee On a Unified High School Science Course,* in 1915, made a second report (18). With the many changes in the high school program taking place, the committee felt that much more experimentation should occur before a final statement about the "unification of sciences" was developed.

In 1913 the *Committee on Natural Sciences* (66) of the National Education Association appointed ten high school teachers, three university professors, three normal school instructors, and one physician to study the high school biology curriculum. After seven meetings the following recommendations were made:

1. That the unity of subject matter in any course in science is of first importance; this is necessary to develop an appreciation of the underlying principles.
2. That the study of biology should concentrate on plants, animals, and man as living organisms.
3. That throughout the course constant references should be made of the applications of biology to human welfare and convenience.
4. That two years of work in "elementary science" should precede work in more advanced science courses; one of these courses should consist of the study of matter and forces of the physical environment; the other of plants and animals (including man) with stress on the applications of science principles to human welfare.

The objectives for the teaching of biology were given as follows:

1. To train the pupil in observation and reasoning.
2. To acquaint each pupil with his environment and the common forms of plant and animal life, together with the structure, function and care of his own body; biological principles would be derived from this study.
3. To show the pupil his place in nature, his share of responsibility in the present and future of human society.

It was strongly recommended that a concept of human welfare underlie all elementary instruction in science.

Several suggestions for the improvement of teaching were made:

1. A variety of teaching methods should be used.
2. Laboratory work should be better structured with less attention to useless drawings, detailed microscopic work and complicated experimentation; the emphasis should be upon the acquisition of knowledge firsthand.

A biology course was designed to include:

1. A study of *plants* with particular attention to their contributions to human welfare.
2. A study of *animals*; life histories, response to the physical and organic environment, continuity of life, and man's place in nature.
3. A study of *man*, including the general structure of the human body, physiology, hygienic care of the body, bacteria and sanitation.

The committee suggested that the principles of human reproduction should form a part of the course, but that instruction in sex hygiene should not be compulsory.

The recommended theme for the course was *human biology*. Thus the work in botany and zoology should be correlated with man and show how he may use his biological knowledge. The course was outlined in three sections so as to be adaptable to either a half-year course in botany, zoology and physiology or a year course in biology.

A year later, 1916, the same committee issued a revised statement on the biology curriculum (67). The objectives were restated as follows:

1. Biology should arouse interest in nature by giving boys and girls firsthand acquaintance with their environment.
2. Biology should emphasize some of the most important applications of science to human welfare.
3. Biology should familiarize pupils with the structure and functions of their own bodies.
4. Biology should give pupils some training in careful observation, in forming logical conclusions, in solving problems and in carrying out projects.
5. Biology should make real to pupils the value of intensive study in any given science as a means through which scientific progress is obtained.

Other ideas were reaffirmed such as, biology should be taught from the point of view of organisms in relation to the inorganic environment, to each other, and in relation to human welfare. Too much time should not be given to a study of the similarities and differences of various types of plants and animals. Instead high school biology teaching should emphasize an elementary conception of the major ideas of biology, the application of these ideas to human progress, and recognition of the great men of biology.

The committee criticized many common teaching practices. Laboratory work that is often done simply to keep students busy and classwork confined to a single text and the four walls of the classroom. "The most important consideration is that the course should be conducted with a live teacher."

A report that was to have considerable influence on the teaching of science was published by the *Commission on the Reorganization of Secondary Education in 1918* (21). The commission defined the aims of secondary education to be: health, command of fundamental processes, worthy home membership, vocation, citizenship, worthy use of leisure, and ethical character. It was expected that all courses in the secondary school would contribute to the realization of these Cardinal Principles of Secondary Education.

The commission members recommended the development of comprehensive high schools in America and a reorganization of the secondary school curriculum. The following statements illustrate their basic ideas:

1. "This commission holds that education is essentially a unitary and continuous process, and that each of the objectives defined above must be recognized throughout the entire extent of secondary education."
2. "Each subject now taught in high schools is in need of extensive reorganization in order that it may contribute more effectively to the objectives outlined herein, and the place of that subject in secondary education should depend upon the value of such contribution."

A special committee, with Otis W. Caldwell as chairman, was appointed by the *Commission on the Reorganization of Secondary Education* to examine the science curriculum in terms of the Cardinal Principles of Secondary Education (19). A *critical* report was prepared which explored all phases of science teaching; only those parts in some way pertinent to the teaching of biology are given here.

A. Guiding principles:
1. The science committee accepted for its general aims the Cardinal Principles of Secondary Education, omitting "the command of fundamental processes."
2. The high school science program should be planned as a whole and with regard to the total high school curriculum.
3. The courses in high school science should constitute the best training for the period regardless of any further science courses the pupil may take.
B. The organization of course work:
1. There should be less attention given to the organization of high school science courses in terms of the logic of the discipline as recognized by the special student of that science. Courses of this nature are better suited to college science.

2. More attention should be given to the development of courses, starting with questions of immediate interest to the pupil and which concern his own life. Topics should be in some kind of progressive order related to the common needs and experiences of young people.
3. Courses need to provide for more self-activity on the part of the student; this can be accomplished by centralizing the work of the course around questions, problems and projects.
4. More attention should be given to selected topics related to local communities, school activities and local industries.

C. Laboratory procedures:
1. Too many experiments merely check generalizations the student already perceives and repeat work given in the text.
2. The data collected are an end in themselves and have no further use.
3. Experiments are minutely quantitative and call for refinements beyond the understanding of secondary school pupils.
4. Laboratory and classroom are separated not only physically but intellectually.
5. Notebook making and notebook records serve no real purpose.

D. Classroom procedures:
1. A problem-project method of science teaching was recommended because it offered promise for better class discussion, more active student participation, and a better opportunity for a "research type" learning.

E. The science course sequence (biology):
1. Biology combined with hygiene was suggested as a ninth grade course in the junior-senior high schools and as a *tenth* grade course in the large comprehensive *four-year high school* Advanced biological courses were recommended for the last two years of high school.

F. Specific recommendations for developing biology courses:
1. Objectives:
    a. Experience derived from World War I emphasizes the need to make health instruction a basic end of education. Since much of biology deals directly with problems of health, this course must accept health instruction as one of its chief and specific ends.

b. The biological sciences should develop within the pupil a purposeful interest in living things.

c. Biology should emphasize some of the most important applications of biological science to human activities, to general and individual human welfare, and especially should familiarize the pupil with the structure and functions of his own body so that he may know why he must live healthfully in order to live happily and usefully.

d. Biology should train the pupil to observe life phenomena accurately and to form logical conclusions through the solution of problems and through projects essential to the productive work of agriculture, gardening, and similar activities.

e. Biology should enrich the life of the pupil through the aesthetic appeal of plants, and animals studied, to the end that he may appreciate and enjoy nature.

f. Biology should demonstrate to the pupil the value of intensive study of biological science as a means to scientific progress. In view of what science means to civilization and in view of the measure to which the methods and results of scientific investigations are today reflected in intelligent thought and action, education in the life sciences for the people of today cannot be ignored.

2. The content of biology.

a. General recommendations:

The course should be a study of living things as they relate to human welfare. Since most of the teachers of biology have been trained in classification and morphology, the tendency has been to teach in the high school a diluted college course cluttered with preserved and dried materials and physiological experiments; ecological studies are seen as more appropriate.

b. Central ideas for a course in biology:

(1) Maintenance of organisms and life of the species.

(2) Interrelationships between different organisms and groups of organisms.

(3) Dependence and interrelations of living things with the physical world.

      (4) Man's control of plants and animals to serve his own ends.
- c. Unifying themes for the biology course:
  - (1) Balance of life and physiological processes.
  - (2) Applications of biology to human welfare and the study of man.
  - (3) Use of local flora and fauna.
3. Procedures for teaching biology:
   - a. A variety of approaches was recognized; however, it was the opinion of the committee that a "topic-project-problem" method organized around centralizing themes offered the best means for achieving the objectives of biology teaching.
   - b. A rich variety of collateral reading is essential to achieve the best learning.
4. The biology laboratory:
   - a. The aim of laboratory instruction should be to develop a consistent chain of significant ideas with the class work, the laboratory serving simply to provide concrete experiences.
   - b. Laboratory work should *precede* textbook assignments under most circumstances.
   - c. Laboratory work is not an end in itself, therefore detailed microscopic work, elaborate drawings, and excessive notebook making are not encouraged.
5. The training of the biology teacher:
   - a. The teacher needs a sound background in biology and scholarship within the field; while research experience is desirable it is not necessarily essential; a special course in the skills and tools for teaching biology is much desired.

Summary 1910–1920

The developments in biology teaching from 1910–1920 reflect suggestions made by earlier committees and a rethinking of the basic issues. A general biology course, in point of view at least, was felt to be the best way to present the biological sciences in high school. During this decade several textbooks appeared on the market under the title of "biology," in contrast to texts on elementary botany, zoology and physiology. Although most committees recommended a synthesis of biological topics not one textbook published between 1910–1920 was organized in this way. Some authors used division titles such as "plant biology," "animal biology," and "human biology" implying an integrated course, but actually the textbook consisted of three distinct sub-courses.

With each succeeding decade the values to be gained from a study of biology have been redefined. At this time the emphasis was upon the teaching of biology for its importance to human welfare—vocations, health, sanitation, avocations, appreciations, understanding of the environment. Physiology came to mean human physiology and hygiene, ecology replaced morphology and the other sections of the course were selected for their use in daily living. The research biologists and the high school biology course parted company at this point.

Biology textbooks published during the 1910–1920 period reflected the growing emphasis upon the applied aspects of biology. The titles of these books were:

Bigelow, M. A., and Bigelow, A. N. 1911. *Applied Biology*. Macmillan Co.
Hunter, G. W. 1911. *Essentials of Biology*. American Book Co.
Peabody, J. E., and Hunt, A. E. 1913. *Elementary Biology*. Macmillan Co.
Hunter, G. W. 1914. *A Civic Biology*. American Book Co.
Gruenberg, B. C. 1916. *Elementary Biology*. Ginn and Co.
Smallwood, Reveley, and Bailey. 1916. *Practical Biology*. Allyn & Bacon.
Hodge, C. F., and Dawson, J. 1918. *Civic Biology*. Ginn and Co.

It had been the recommendation of most committees that biology be made a more "practical"course. The "miniature college course" taught in high school was thought unsuitable for the average tenth-grade pupil.

Teaching methods advocated during this period were of the nature that called for more active participation by the student. Projects, problems, and questions were seen as a way to increase student involvement. Wider reading, field trips, use of community resources and the study of local flora and fauna were regarded as techniques for improving motivation.

Teachers and scientists alike felt that students in high school should learn about the nature of science. The organization of courses around problems and projects was an effort to develop some understanding of the methods of science. A study of the lives of famous biologists was felt to create an appreciation for the scientific enterprise. While this objective was educationally sound and the methods of attainment promising, the results were disappointing.

Each committee reporting during this period suggested that the broad "ideas" or "principles" of biology should be stressed. The rationale was aptly expressed by M. W. Morse (55): "Living things, after all, partake of the same general characteristics."

The type of laboratory work offered in high school biology courses was severely criticized by the reporting committees. The work was seen as an "end in itself," "busy work," "uninteresting to students," and frequently "unrelated to class activities." In the popular literature on biology teaching the argument continued to be "Living" versus "Dead" biology. Those in favor of living biology were the most vocal. While the science committees suggested more contact with living organisms, classroom practices indicated an overwhelming study of "dead" biology.

Although curriculum making in science continued to be a cooperative effort of professional scientists, science teachers and educators, the ratio of participating groups changed. The membership of the two best known committees on science teaching— the *Committee of Ten* (1892) and the *Committee on the Reorganization of Science in Secondary Schools* (1920)—were as follows:

1892 Committee (10 members)	*1920 Committee (47 members)*
5—College or university professors and/or scientists	24—High school teachers or administrators
3—High school teachers	11—College or university professors and/or scientists
1—Normal school teacher	6—Normal school teachers
1—Superintendent of schools	5—Superintendents of schools
	1—Business representative

It is apparent that public school personnel had a greater involvement in the construction of science courses in 1920 than in 1892 and that representatives from colleges and universities had less potential influence.

Enrollments in the biological sciences changed rapidly between 1910–1915, the number of pupils taking biology increased from 7,883 in 1910 to 80,403 by 1915. These figures represent an increase from 1.1 per cent of the high school population taking biology in 1910 to 6.9 per cent in 1915. Between 1910–1915 the enrollment in physiology dropped from 15.3 to 9.5 per cent; in zoology the decrease was from 6.9 to 3.2 per cent; and in botany the loss was from 15.8 to 9.1 per cent of the secondary school enrollment. Among the secondary school sciences—biology, botany, zoology, physiology, physics and chemistry—general biology is to be the only high school science course which in the years to come will show a consistent increase in enrollment, as regards both the percentage of pupils enrolled in high school and the actual number taking the course.

Data on the number of pupils in general science, a new course introduced in the period 1910–1920, are not available before 1920. In the years to come, however, it is to keep pace in enrollment growth along with biology.

Both general science and general biology were courses that broke with tradition in an attempt to provide a more comprehensive "picture" of science and to meet the educational needs in science for a larger portion of the high school population. The popularity of these subjects with young people is reflected in the enrollment trends. In the textbooks written for these courses one finds a greater emphasis upon the "practical" and the "applied" aspects of each subject. This movement was also evident in the teaching of physics and chemistry. Textbooks on "household" physics and "household" chemistry, intended for use by the ordinary student, were published but did not long remain in favor.

There were those who felt that the "new" type of science courses were unsound in point of view, educational value and in course content. Possibly the most vocal of the opponents was John Dewey. In an address before the science section of the National Education Association in New York City in March,

1916, he commented on the selection of content for science courses as follows (28):

> One method is the scrappy one of picking up isolated materials just because they happen to be familiar objects within the pupil's experience, and of merely extending and deepening the range of pupil's familiarity, and then passing on to something else. No amount of this will make an introduction to education, to say nothing of science, for an introduction leads or draws into a subject, while this method never, save by accident, gets the pupil within range of problems and exploratory methods of science. The other erroneous course is taken when the teacher's imagination is so limited that he cannot conceive of science existing except in the definitely segregated areas, concepts and terms which are found in books under the heads of physics, chemistry, etc., and who is thus restricted to move within these boundaries. Such a person forgets that there is no material in existence which is physical or chemical or botanical, but that a certain subject matter *becomes* physical or chemical or botanical when certain questions are raised, and when it is subjected to certain modes of inquiry. What is desired of the pupil is that starting from the ordinary unclassed material of experience he shall acquire command of the points of view, the ideas and methods, which *make* it physical or chemical or whatever.

He continues his criticism with remarks about the education rationale underlying the "general science courses":

> The entire cogency of their position depends upon the identification of science with a certain limited field of subject matter, ignoring the fact that science is primarily the method of intelligence at work in observation, in inquiry and experimental testing; that, fundamentally, what science means and stands for is simply the best ways yet found out by which human intelligence can do the work it should do, ways that are continually improved by the very process of use.

It was to take more than forty years before this interpretation of the nature of education in biology was to find expression in a curriculum movement.

V

A Period of Curriculum Refinement, 1920–1930

THE DECADE following the close of World War I was a time in which biology curriculum makers attempted to implement the education theory developed earlier. The influence of the *Commission on the Reorganization of Secondary Education* (1920) and the work of the related *Committee on the Reorganization of Science* is seen throughout the 1920–1930 period. These reports immediately stimulated local committees to re-examine their biology curriculum in light of the Cardinal Principles of Secondary Education, as defined by the Commission on the Reorganization of Secondary Education.

In 1923, a committee under the chairmanship of George W. Hunter of Knox College, reported on a new biology course for the State of Illinois (40). The Illinois group concurred with the objectives of the *Committee on the Reorganization of Science*. Much concern was expressed, however, about the kind of curriculum materials prepared by the research biologists and their failure to consider the interests and needs of the adolescent. This group, therefore, decided to base its curriculum deliberations on comments received from 2,500 first-year high school students. Their interests were found to be centered around problems relating to:

1. Improvement of environmental conditions
2. Health
3. Working and structure of the human body
4. Economic importance of certain biological materials
5. Interpretation of factors related to the students' environment
6. Habits of efficiency
7. Sex understanding and sex health
8. Worthy citizenship

To a lesser extent young people were found to be interested in the strange, bizarre and unusual in nature, classification and evolution. A pragmatic point of view underlay the reasons for their likes and dislikes, a view the biology committee felt should not be overlooked.

A list of 98 biological topics was developed to encompass the interests expressed by the 2,500 high school students; these topics were then organized into nine teaching units to form the following biology course:

1. Living things in relation to their environment
2. Interdependence of living things
3. Life processes in plants and animals
4. Green plants as living organisms
5. Animals as living organisms
6. Responses of plants and animals
7. Reproduction of plants and animals
8. Evolution
9. Man's control of his environment

In 1924, the *Committee for Reorganization of the Biological Sciences* of the Cleveland Biology Teachers Club reported on a new curriculum for biology teaching (68). Their tentative outline for a tenth-grade required biology course was stated in terms of major ideas to be developed:

1. There is a fundamental resemblance between plants and animals (protoplasm and cell structure).
2. There is an interrelationship of plants and animals (the web of life, adaptation and the interrelations of plants and animals).
3. The work of higher plants has led to a differentiation of parts and a division of labor among cells (plant structure and adaptation to specific environments).
4. Green plants are the foundations of the world's food supply (manufacture of carbohydrates, proteins and fats, assimilation, respiration and growth).
5. The oxygen, carbon and nitrogen cycles influence the welfare of plants and animals.
6. The problem of food getting has led to special adaptations

among plants and animals (parasitism, characteristic habits of organisms, protective coloration, mimicry).

7. The food requirements of plants and animals relate them closely to man (relation of insects to human welfare, insects and human disease, microorganisms and their relation to infectious diseases).
8. The assimilation of food has led to a differentiation and division of labor among cells (digestion, respiration, circulation, excretion, and the nervous system).
9. There is a continuity of life, whether plant or animal (asexual and sexual reproduction).
10. Life shows progress, the present may be interpreted in terms of the past (evolution: explanation and evidences).
11. Man may control the production of forms and has within his power the improvement of both plants and animals (laws of inheritance: relation to plant and animal improvement including man).

The committee also outlined a twelfth-grade botany course to include: 1) fundamental differences between plants and animals; 2) structure of plants; 3) nutrition and photosynthesis; 4) reproduction; 5) evolution of plants; 6) identification; 7) plant breeding; 8) forests and conservation; 9) beautification of home surroundings; 10) life history of important plants; 11) field trips to parks, farms, sugar factories, and other areas of biological interest.

The Cleveland committee accepted the philosophy of the *Commission on Reorganization of Secondary Education* (1920), in developing both the tenth and twelfth grade courses.

In 1924, the *Committee on the Place of Sciences in Education* of the American Association for the Advancement of Science reported its study on the problems of science teaching (20). The twenty-one members represented a variety of scientific and educational societies, university and industrial scientists, high school science teachers and laymen; four biological societies were represented. It was generally felt that there should be a clearer understanding of the purposes of science instruction in schools. These purposes should be based upon sound educational and scientific observation and experimentation so as to give them "a factual basis worthy of the spirit of science."

Following a survey of science programs in secondary schools and junior colleges the committtee reported a widespread interest in securing a closer relation between these two levels of education. A recommendation was made that a science program should be formulated for schools but not in the direction of fostering a stringent standardization.

The committee recognized a need for . . . "a synthesis of sciences, general views, and a common interpretation of the meaning of science. We need to develop this synthetic interpretation without using or reducing specialization." At another place in the report:

> May we not come to sense an interlocking of various fields of knowledge, a trained feeling for the value and significance of 'things in general' based upon but rising much above the results of our own specific scientific studies? In our necessary separate specialization have we not reached a point where we must climb upon some sort of vantage position and get the whole landscape again and often?

The problem of science courses for the training of teachers was debated. Most university science courses were recognized as useful for specialists in a particular science but not suitable for the best training of high school teachers.

> The normal school and teachers college situation is important. In spite of the limitations of these institutions the brief general courses given often provide a general foundation which is very different but probably no worse than the highly differentiated and unbalanced college work in the sciences.

Among the other recommendations for the improvement of education in science were:

1. The need for publications popularizing science.
2. The need to develop a series of specific illustrations of how the scientist's method of working may be useful in the common affairs of people in non-scientific pursuits.
3. The need for an "adequate technique for assembling, classifying and interpreting objectives. If they may not be made

harmonious, all points of view may be fairly presented, so that in one report science men may find a well-balanced presentation of the various purposes now held in mind by those who have clearly defined objectives for their work."
4. The need to define what modern science is trying to do.
5. The need for better trained high school and college teachers.

The AAAS Committee reviewed many problems of science teaching, from course objectives to teacher training. The report was one of the first to suggest that some of the problems might be solved by the development of a program of research in science education. An extensive bibliography on the teaching of science in high school was prepared; one section was specifically on biology teaching. The bibliography was published by the Department of the Interior, Bureau of Education, Washington, D.C., as Bulletin, 1925, No. 13—*Bibliography of Science Teaching in Secondary Schools.* 161 p.

In March, 1927, the *Committee on Standards for Use in the Reorganization of Secondary School Curriculum* (74) of the North Central Association reported its deliberations on the objectives for the teaching of secondary school science as follows: "The objectives have been derived or determined through an analysis of the ideas, attitudes, interests, and activities of individuals in everyday life, and of society as found in operation in past and present conditions." They were described as follows:

A.   The *ultimate* objectives of science teaching:
   1. To maintain health and physical fitness.
   2. To use leisure time in right ways.
   3. To sustain successfully certain definite social relationships such as civic, domestic, community and the like.
   4. To engage in exploratory-vocational and vocational activities.
B. The *immediate* objectives of science teaching:
   1. Acquiring fruitful knowledge:
      a. Which is preparatory to acquiring other knowledge.
      b. Which functions directly in developing dispositions and abilities.

    c. Which is useful in the control of situations of everyday life.

2. Developing attitudes, interests, motives, ideals and appreciations:

    a. To develop an appreciation of the lawfulness of nature, and the attitude that the student is bound to conform to such laws.

    b. To develop an appreciation of the work of great scientists.

3. Developing definite mental techniques in perception, memory, imagination, judgment, and reasoning:

    a. To guide pupils in the solution of problems as a means of practice in scientific thinking.

    b. To develop the ability to apply principles to the interpretation of common phenomena.

    c. To be able to discriminate between good and poor experimental procedure.

4. Acquiring right habits and useful skills:

    a. To develop "ideals of accuracy in observation, clarity in expression, habits of orderliness in arranging data, of suspended judgment until the evidence is adequate, skill in selecting data in convincing form, in drawing conclusions."

A subcommittee on the teaching of biology (74), under the chairmanship of E. R. Downing, University of Chicago, was of the opinion that biology teaching could contribute to all the objectives stated by the general committee. It felt that it was unwise to attempt to teach too many things and that only biological principles of maximum social value and interest should be taught. The committee then outlined in detail examples of "useful or worthwhile" knowledge and classroom techniques that would contribute to the attainment of each particular objective.

At another time E. R. Downing commented (30) that: "A biology course should consist of not only what is good, but of what is best. Time is too short to fritter it away on what is inconsequential."

In 1928, the American Association for the Advancement of Science, through its special *Committee on Science in Education*, published a report "On the Place of Science in Education." (65)

The twenty-nine committee members included representatives from eight universities, seven teachers colleges, medical schools, the National Education Association, Science Service, various foundations and one high school teacher.

The committee had been appointed to formulate a statement on the place of science in general education in schools and colleges with respect to the lives of people outside of school. After reviewing developments in science and the impact of science on man's life the conclusion was reached that: "Science instruction both in school and out needs better organization, more effective cooperation to make even the health knowledge now available function more completely in the lives of people generally." The major ideas reported were:

1. The citizen uses science both in conclusions and method for each day's work; he should profit, therefore, from what he understands of scientific facts, principles and occurrences. Possession of scientific knowledge or of the applications resulting from this knowledge must carry with it a knowledge of the proper uses of these possessions; "a sense of moral obligation that will prevent the newly acquired knowledge and method of science serving base ends."

2. The understanding and applications of both scientific knowledge and methods to new situations must be made the immediate objectives of school and college effort. There is an acute need to get more science into the school program because of the unparalleled growth and use of science knowledge. The committee encouraged the tendency toward a coherent and cumulative secondary school sequence in science subjects.

3. It is time to re-study the whole situation of science in secondary schools owing to the widespread growth of general science in the junior high schools.

4. After reviewing a number of research studies on curriculum and learning in the teaching of science, the following resolution was adopted: "These studies represent but a beginning in the application of the objectives of scientific method to the problems of science teaching. Such investigations must be

multiplied and verified by those truly interested in the scientific solution of such questions."

5. It was felt that the teaching of science was not entirely effective because educational procedures are too hasty; in the hurry to achieve, those arduous endeavors by means of which lasting results may alone be developed are omitted. Education also fails because it so often misses the main purpose of teaching modern scientific thought and controls.

6. Science is not primarily for the purpose of building dynamos, understanding radio, and producing more corn or better hogs, but for producing better human beings. Teaching for this purpose should include some of the moral responsibilities that go with the achievement of scientific knowledge.

7. Science teachers need to develop a point of view about science. Most have had too little real science study. The committee suggested that science courses for those who are to teach need to be developed with their teaching uses in mind, to the same extent that special courses are developed for those who intend to practice law or medicine; "we need a similar organization in the use of science courses for those who are to teach." It was pointed out that this did not mean less exacting courses but redirected courses relating to the professional uses of science in education. It was recommended that college courses for teachers be developed with a professional outlook instead of restricting them to subjects with only the research outlook. The recommendation of the committee was that "a more thorough-going preparation in the fundamentals of science is needed by all who aspire to teach it."

8. In their discussions the committee noted that neither the methods of scientific study nor the personalities of those who apply them have been objectified with sufficient clarity to make them functional in general education. Even though objectives of science teaching for the past 75 years have had references to "the scientific method," there has been little transmission to young people of how scientists work and study, or even of scientific attitudes. It seems that the schools and society are absorbing the output of scientific work, that is, the practical application, much more rapidly than they are absorbing the culture of the men who contributed it. A liberal education

is incomplete without this culture. The following resolution was adopted: "Science as method is quite as important as science as subject matter, and should receive much attention in science instruction."

9. Other recommendations made by the committee were that: (a) a study be made of the situation, tendencies and needs of science instruction in educational systems; (b) the services of a field secretary be secured to work with existing agencies, to distribute information on research in science education, to stimulate further research, to operate as a sort of clearing-house agent, and to continue the organization of new groups of science teachers and writers for the popularization of science; (c) a national council of science teachers be organized to advance science teaching, to increase public appreciation of science and to secure for science teachers better facilities for teaching.

Summary 1920–1930

It became clear during this period that the special sciences (biology, chemistry, and physics) in the high school must justify their contribution to the over-all education of students. The *Cardinal Principles of Secondary Education* provided the frame of reference toward which all science teaching was expected to make contributions.

The movement to "humanize" the study of biology, which had been gaining momentum for several decades, was by now a generally accepted point of view for curriculum makers. The report of the *American Association for the Advancement of Science* in 1928 lent further support in this direction.

One change in the purposes for teaching science deserves special mention. Many scientists at this time expressed the opinion that the central purpose of education in science should be the development of an understanding of the nature of science, its methods, attitudes and cultural impact. As a result much educational research in the succeeding years was directed toward identifying the elements of the scientific methods and scientific attitudes.

The need for a continuing research program on science teaching was recognized by the *American Association for the Advancement of Science* but specific suggestions for implementing the program were not developed. The same situation existed concerning appropriate courses in the colleges and universities for the training of science teachers. Unfortunately this was to be the role of the professional scientist for many years to come in science education, an advisor but not a participant, suggesting but not supporting.

The popular literature on biology teaching for the 1920–1930 period contained many references on the importance of emphasizing the basic principles of biology with correspondingly less attention to the study of the specific organism. Several textbooks published during the period made claims that the text emphasized principles, but only a slight difference can be noted between these and textbooks that did not make this claim.

Not apparent from the committee reports of this decade were the efforts to develop a "standard" course in biology. There were surveys and studies to find the common elements of biology courses and to identify the basic principles of biology. This was the period of the standardized test which in turn demanded fairly uniform courses of study if the tests were to be valid.

The 1920–1930 period in biological education was not an exciting one from the standpoint of new developments. But the enrollment in high school biology continued to mushroom and the course became increasingly prominent in the secondary school curriculum.

VI

A Period of Questioning, 1930–1940

THE DEPRESSION YEARS in America produced the usual questioning of educational practices that characterizes a time of economic or social crisis. The teaching of science was extensively examined by a number of influential organizations as well as by the Federal government. Significant reports were issued by: *The National Society for the Study of Education*; *The Progressive Education Association*; and the *National Association for Research in Science Teaching*. A survey on *Instruction in Science* was conducted by the Office of Education, United States Department of the Interior. Four books on the teaching of high school biology were published during this decade and the *National Association of Biology Teachers* was founded.

The 1930's represented a time in education when attention was focused upon the individual student and his personal, social and economic welfare. The major criterion for the selection of course content was "to meet the needs of students." It was also a time when schools took over functions that had previously belonged to parents. Health information and consumership loomed large in the biology curriculum.

Mechanization in farming, automation in the factory and the growing assortment of electrical appliances in the home all helped to make people aware of "science." The reaction was not always a sympathetic one and arguments for a moratorium on science were frequent. Those interested in the teaching of science were called upon to justify its purpose in the secondary school curriculum. Three factors contributed to the demand for a clearer statement of "why teach science": problems associated with a larger fraction of students entering high school, the cost of teaching science, and a changing philosophy of secondary education.

The biology committee of the *North Central Association of*

Colleges and Secondary Schools submitted two reports in 1931, one a general report on the teaching of biology (31) and an investigation on the time needed to teach particular units (32). Members of the committee expressed the opinion that one's knowledge of science was serviceable in life only if it was acquired or retained in the form of principles or generalizations. Even then, practice in the application of biological principles to problematic situations must be given if the knowledge is to possess either intellectual or practical value. The biological principles for a high school course should be selected from those most important in the day-to-day life of young people and adults. Examples the committee had in mind were:

1. The adaptation of organisms to their environment.
2. The germ nature of disease.
3. The interdependence of organisms.
4. The cell as a structural and physiological unit of living things.
5. The principle of evolution.
6. The distinctive characteristics of living things.

The first step in curriculum planning was to select significant biological principles to provide the framework for the course. The second step was to select "problematic life situations" that create a need for biological principles for their solution; principles therefore would not be taught in a manner that leads to memorization. The committee recommended that: "A few principles taught to the point of mastery such that they will function in life, constitute a better course in biology than a mass of detailed facts or even a larger number of principles learned only to be forgotten."

To determine some reasonable estimates of the length of time it takes for students to develop an understanding of a biology principle, the committee prepared teaching units to be taught in twenty high schools. Wide differences were found among classes in the length of time required for "mastery" of the principles contained in the unit. A tentative conclusion was that it took about four weeks for a high school student to develop a fair understanding of a significant biological principle.

While the committee felt the "principles approach" to be sound and practical as a focus of biology teaching, it was not optimistic about influencing high school teaching practices for the following reasons:

1. Teachers are not interested in spending the time essential to developing an understanding of a principle, but choose to have students memorize large masses of unorganized facts.
2. College entrance examinations consist primarily of questions that require only the recall of facts to answer.
3. College science classes are not taught from the point of view of the consumer of science; teachers are therefore not prepared to make use of science as it applies to problems encountered by young people and adults.
4. Students are not taught how to use their knowledge of science in problematic situations.

Instruction in Science, a survey of science teaching practices was published by the Office of Education, United States Department of the Interior, in 1933 (10). Parts of the survey bearing upon the teaching of biology are presented here to provide a background of existing conditions in biology teaching at the start of the 1930–1940 decade.

Thirty-two courses of study in biology were examined for statements of objectives. Among the objectives most frequently listed were the following:

1. To acquire knowledge that will produce a better understanding of our environment.
2. To acquire knowledge which will function to achieve the Cardinal Principles of Secondary Education.
3. To develop an appreciation of nature and of one's responsibility in the world.
4. To acquire knowledge of the fundamental principles of biology.
5. To acquire an interest in nature.
6. To develop the ability to think scientifically.

In forty of forty-five courses of biology examined the content was divided into three major divisions: botany, zoology and physiology. Their organization under these sections was "similar to the special courses from which they were taken."

Visits to the classes of biology teachers revealed that most of the questions asked of students could be answered in one word and referred to the parts of either an animal or a plant. When the teachers were asked, "How do you train pupils to think scientifically?" none gave an answer sufficiently clear to indicate to the investigator what was actually being done in this direction. The test samples collected from each school measured only the student's ability to remember isolated facts. The biology laboratory work was typically the copying of pictures from the textbook.

The study as a whole revealed that:

1. There was little curriculum planning based upon a clear-cut theory of education.
2. Data available from research studies on science teaching were not used.
3. There was a need for more study upon grade placement and for learning studies on science teaching.
4. Biology teachers were the least able of all science teachers to identify their purposes for teaching the course.

Some of the recommendations for improving the teaching of science were:

1. The use of concepts as centers of organization in courses.
2. A shift from a topical to a problem approach in teaching.
3. The use of more supervised study with less time spent upon oral recitations.

It was found that courses of study prepared with the guidance of supervisors or consultants were superior to those prepared exclusively by classroom teachers. This suggests that curriculum planning requires some special insights, particularly with regard to the development of a correlated program of science in high schools.

In 1932, *A Program for Teaching Science* was developed by a committee under the chairmanship of S. Ralph Powers and sponsored by the National Society for the Study of Education

(70). The 364-page report explored almost every question on science teaching from the kindergarten to the college level. More attention was given to the establishment of a point of view on science teaching, the psychology of learning, and curriculum theory, than can be found in committee reports up to this time. Among the major contributions of the committee were: 1) the support given to the development of a twelve-year program of science teaching in the schools; 2) the plan for organizing courses around the principles and generalizations of science; and 3) the emphasis on the importance of teaching the methods of science as an integral part of classroom instruction.

In the outline that follows, some of the committee's concepts about science teaching are listed:

A. Theory of science education:
   1. Science teaching should contribute to the major aim of education, "Life Enrichment through Participation in a Democratic Social Order."
   2. The program of science teaching should be continuous from the elementary school to the university.
   3. "In a program of general education ... the work of instruction will be directed toward increasing the understanding of those principles and generalizations of science that have had the largest application in molding the character of our society and of those which have within them potentialities for influence in the future."
   4. An education program for an age of science will recognize the content and the method of science. Science teaching should provide a rich experience which makes positive demands upon the use of the methods of science for the solution of problems. Desirable "scientific" attitude should also result from this experience.
   5. The usefulness of subject matter is measured by the extent to which it touches the interests and relates to the welfare of human beings; and the extent to which it assists an individual to adapt to the human society of which he is a part.
B. Aims and objectives of science education:
   1. "The principles and generalizations that ramify most widely

into human affairs may be stated as objectives of science education."

2. Educational values from science teaching will have been attained if students acquire:

   a. "... an ability to utilize the findings of science that have application to their experiences;

   b. An ability to interpret the natural phenomena of their environment;

   c. An appreciation of scientific attitudes through an understanding of, and ability to use, some of the methods of study that have been used by creative workers in the field of science."

C. Selection of course content in science:

1. The content should include problems which are real to students and will provide practice in the use of scientific methods.

2. The content should contribute to the major generalizations of science and also relate to the welfare of human beings.

3. Content should be chosen for its practical as well as for its cultural or liberalizing values.

4. The content selected should have not only immediate values to the pupil but also potential values in adulthood.

5. Content should be selected to provide for pupils of different interests and capacities.

D. Organization of science courses:

1. The content should be organized into units representing major problems of everyday life.

2. The content should be organized to focus on the interrelation of science and society.

3. The content should be organized to provide a means to problem solving and to give experience in the methods of science.

E. Classroom teaching procedures:

1. "The demonstrations, the laboratory experiment, the field trip, the reading of textbook and science reference books, the examination of visual aids, and similar activities should be considered primarily as sources of experiences that provide the bases for reflection in problem situations and not as ends in themselves."

2. "Pupil-committee reports, group demonstrations, class discussion, class debates, and science club activities are types of

group enterprises that are encouraged as learning experiences of value in humanizing and socializing the science work."

3. A wide variety of learning activities should be used within the class with the work individualized as much as possible.

4. Extensive reading from a variety of sources should be a characteristic feature of the classwork.

5. At the end of each unit students should be provided with activities in which they are given the opportunity to *organize* and *synthesize* the ideas acquired in the preceding stages of the unit.

6. Time and emphasis given to the various units should be determined by the social value of the unit, its "teachability" and "learnability," the teacher's and pupil's interest in the unit, the local significance of the unit, and its value to other units of the course.

F. Laboratory procedures:

1. The laboratory work should be an integral part of problem solving and have the characteristics of "experience-getting" rather than illustrative or confirmatory work.

2. The laboratory should be used for the purpose of developing better understanding and interpretations of the principles of science.

3. It is not a question of individual laboratory work or teacher demonstration, but which method produces the outcomes expected of pupils in terms of the specific situation. A full appreciation and understanding of the scientific method demands that the student gain experience with experimental procedures and develop skills in laboratory techniques.

G. Testing and evaluation in science:

1. Tests should ascertain the intellectual growth and status of the pupil and consist of more than an inventory of detailed facts.

2. Tests should give an indication of the degree to which pupils have attained the objectives of the course; attitudes, appreciations, skills in thinking and learning and the depth of interest.

H. Sequence of course offerings:

1. The committee recommended a continuous correlated science program extending from the first grade through the senior high school.

2. The committee suggested the following curriculum pattern in science:

Grades I–VI   —Elementary science

Grades VII–IX—General science

Grade X   —Biological science or physical science (physics)

Grade XI   —First-year physical science (physics) or first-year biological science; second-year biological science or second-year physical science (chemistry)

Grade XII   —Elective selected from those listed under the offerings for tenth and eleventh grades and such other electives as the school may choose to offer

After establishing a basis for education in the sciences, the committee then considered the special subjects. A course in general biology was recognized as preferable to separate courses in botany and zoology, because of the likelihood of a greater emphasis on fundamental biological principles.

An understanding of the following biological principles was considered fundamental in a secondary school course:

1. Energy cannot be created or destroyed but merely transformed from one form to another.
2. The ultimate source of energy of all living things is sunlight.
3. Microorganisms are the immediate cause of some diseases.
4. All organisms must be adjusted to the environmental factors in order to survive in the struggle for existence.
5. All life comes from pre-existing life and reproduces its own kind.
6. Animals and plants are not distributed uniformly nor at random over the surface of the earth, but are found in definite zones and in local societies.
7. Food, oxygen, certain optimal conditions of temperature, moisture and light are essential to the life of most living things.
8. The cell is a structural and physiological unit in all organisms.
9. The more complex organisms have been derived by natural

processes from simpler ones these in turn from still simpler, and so on back to the first living forms.

The committee members examined a number of widely used biology textbooks and found only a small portion of the texts were devoted to developing an understanding of these biological principles.

The committee felt that course work should be organized: 1) to develop an understanding of a biological principle by means of teaching units representing a small mass of essential learning material; 2) to afford abundant drill in the application of biological principles to life problems; and 3) to contribute to the attainment of scientific attitudes, the methods and safeguards of scientific thinking.

In 1932 the Progressive Education Association, through its commission on Secondary School Curriculum, established the *Committee on the Function of Science in General Education* (22). The Committee published a 579-page report on science teaching in 1938. Previous to publication its tentative findings were submitted "to numerous groups of science teachers drawn from different geographical regions and working under widely varying conditions" for critical examination.

This study was addressed primarily to teachers of science, but the committee felt that the "report bears import for a far wider group, first, because of the way in which it approaches its problem specifically and explicitly through an examination into the goals of general education in the secondary school . . .; and second, because the function of science teaching cannot be performed by teachers of science alone . . . but calls upon the understanding and insightful cooperation of teachers in many if not all of the other areas of the school." The primary concern was the contribution *science* could make to the education of young people and therefore the special subject fields were not considered. Sample teaching units were prepared, however, in biology and other science courses to provide "concrete examples of learning experiences selected and organized in accordance with the principles stated in the report."

The committee was primarily interested in trying "to formulate a useful theory of science teaching growing out of what it believes can and should be done rather than out of what it sees actually being done . . ." It was assumed throughout the report "that educational processes and goals must be relevant to the needs of the learner as he interacts with his social medium . . ."

Among the major ideas expressed were the following:

A. Theory of science education:
   1. "The purpose of general education is to meet the needs of individuals in the basic aspects of living in such a way as to promote the fullest possible realization of personal potentialities and the most effective participation in a democratic society."
   2. The needs of adolescents were divided into four basic aspects of living:
      a. Personal living
      b. Immediate personal-social relations
      c. Social-civic relationships
      d. Economic relationships
B. The learning of science:
   1. "What the individual does in any situation depends primarily on the urge he is attempting to satisfy, the tension he is trying to resolve. The terms in which the tension exists *for him* significantly determine his behavior."
   2. "The human organism must be thought of as operating always in relationship to its environment. To think of the individual apart from his environment is in fact to deal with an abstraction."
   3. Emphasis was placed upon the "continuous reconstruction of experience" of the learner as the essence of education. "Learning takes place through the reorganization of the individual's present behavior patterns (or 'wholes') into more inclusive, more adequate, patterns by bringing together any 'elements' that have meaningful relation both to the individual's behavior pattern and to the situation at hand."
   4. ". . . that the learning process is integrally bound up with the individual's emotional life, as well as with his physical and intellectual life, and that the whole individual must be under-

stood and dealt with adequately if learning is to be effective and satisfying."

5. In the field of science instruction the emphasis in learning was in "terms of larger understandings with analysis and synthesis going on simultaneously, and upon reflective thinking in which induction and deduction are both utilized. Factual information, drill, and memorization are to be subordinated to more significant goals."

C. Aims and objectives of science teaching:

1. To acquire understanding in science as distinguished from information. ("The term 'understanding' is here used to denote a major conception so grasped as to illuminate its connections with related conceptions and to result in significant changes in the individual's behavior.")

2. To develop the ability to think reflectively:
   a. To recognize the nature of a problem.
   b. To develop a hypothesis in terms of past experiences.
   c. To marshal evidence.
   d. To perceive the crucial tests of a hypothesis.
   e. To devise experimental conditions.
   f. To express conclusions unambiguously.

3. To develop particular skills or abilities related to problem solving:
   a. Setting up experimental apparatus.
   b. Using measuring instruments.
   c. Recognizing sources of error in observation.
   d. Getting the sense of a written passage.
   e. Using libraries and other sources of graphic information.
   f. Assessing the reliability of authorities.
   g. Expressing hypotheses accurately and economically.
   h. Using mathematical procedures.
   i. Conducting discussion in ways to bring the main issues to the forefront.

4. To develop certain attitudes and dispositions useful in problem solving in science.
   a. Active curiosity.
   b. Caution in making generalizations.
   c. Tolerance of new ideas and suggestions.
   d. Disposition to try a variety of approaches and points of view on a problem.

e. Confidence that scientific methods will be successful in solving problems.

f. Disposition to see a problem through to its conclusion in spite of distractions.

g. Readiness to act on the basis of tentative judgments.

5. Meeting the needs of adolescents in the following aspects of living:

a. Personal living—(Personal health, self-assurance, philosophy of life, range of personal interests, aesthetic satisfactions and a satisfactory world picture.)

b. Immediate personal-social relationships—(Increasingly mature relationships in home and family and with adults outside the family; successful and increasingly mature relationships with age mates of both sexes.)

c. Social-civic relationships—(Responsible participation in socially significant activities and social recognition.)

d. Economic relationships—(Emotional assurance of progress toward adult status; guidance in choosing an occupation and for vocational preparation; wise selection and use of goods and services; effective action in solving basic economic problems.)

D. Criteria for the selection of content in science courses:

1. Does the work help the adolescent to meet his personal-social needs in the four categories?

2. Does it help the adolescent to develop the characteristics of personality essential to effective living in a democratic society and tend to further the realization of the ideals of a democratic society?

3. Are the problems real and stimulating to the adolescent?

4. Do the problems offer an opportunity for experiences in the methods of reflective thinking?

5. Does the work offer the student an opportunity to be creative?

6. Are the problems of a wide enough range to meet the needs of different individuals and of different communities?

E. Classroom procedures:

1. No single plan of teaching was endorsed. "Procedures should be kept flexible and experimental in character, always with a careful appraisal of results to the purposes to which the school is committed."

2. Teachers may find it desirable to develop "source units" on science problems. The details of the problems and the method of attack should be cooperatively planned by the students and teacher.

3. The generalizations and inquiries used in building the science curriculum should be stated as working ideas, and be of an interpretive nature rather than pure science.

4. Pupil rather than teacher activity should dominate in the class; the teacher's function in learning is one of guidance.

F. Laboratory procedure:
1. Laboratory experiences exemplify the scientific method and should be developed to incorporate research procedures.

2. Science problems developed in the classroom should demand laboratory experience for their solution.

3. Students should be encouraged to devise their own experiments.

G. Testing and evaluation:
1. The purpose of evaluation is to determine growth toward desirable characteristics of personality; and in terms of the subject, growth in understanding.

2. The real measure of learning is to be found in the student's conduct in life situations. Objective tests cannot be the sole measure of his progress and development.

3. The steps in the construction of implements for evaluation are:
   a. A clear statement of the objectives of the course.
   b. A description of the kinds of student behavior that indicate growth toward achievement of science objectives.
   c. Invention of methods of observing and recording the behavior that indicates progress toward achievement of the objectives.

H. Science courses:
1. The committee does not suggest, nor endorse, either a particular sequence of courses or separate science courses.

2. The type of course and the organization found useful in attaining the objectives, herein outlined, suggest a *unified core* or a *broad fields course* in terms of the major understandings of science rather than a science curriculum composed of special subjects, such as biology, chemistry and physics.

Some of the characteristic recommendations of the committee were: 1) the democratic way of life constitutes the goals of education; 2) the concept of science teaching exists within the context of general education rather than contributing to it; 3) the need to develop the personal-social characteristics of students, as well as intellectual interests; 4) courses should be organized around large units of human experience, rather than the logic of the subject; 5) the personal-social needs of students should be the point of departure in curriculum construction; 6) functional or operative science instruction is sought rather than the memorization of masses of facts; 7) results of evaluation should be used in the guidance of students toward the goals of science teaching.

The National Association for Research in Science Teaching, through its *Committee on Secondary School Science*, published a report, in 1938, on practices and points of view in secondary school science instruction covering grades seven through twelve (42). The report was developed from 79 responses to a questionnaire addressed to "highly selected specialists in the field of secondary school science teaching" and "a few selected curriculum specialists." "The findings represent strictly the opinions of competent specialists in the field of secondary-school science teaching with respect to better practices. It is in no sense an indication of what the majority of science teachers think should be better practices nor what they are doing in their classrooms."

The summary of the study is presented in outline form and includes only the items which receive a weighted 95% agreement or over; the wording of the committee has been used in most statements, others have been briefed.

    A. Point of view on science teaching:
        1. Science in secondary schools shall be considered as:
            a. A method of thought and procedure.
            b. A living experience.
        2. The implications of science in modern civilization demand that—
            a. Secondary school science content shall be modified from present practice to include materials of greater social significance.

b. The methods of teaching should be markedly altered toward greater emphasis on attitudes of mind, methods of thinking and working, and the social implications of these aspects.

c. Secondary science is but one phase of a continuing process of education which begins early in life and continues for many through college. Hence there is a need at all levels for constant integration and articulation, not only with the other aspects of science education, but with the other phases of general education.

d. Science instruction should be arranged in a continuous and dependent sequence from the primary grades to the end of high school.

B. Psychology of learning:

1. Experience with natural phenomena and the applications of science shall lead to the formulation of conclusions related to those broad generalizations which have the largest application in human interests.

2. The problems and situations through which the learner attains the objectives sought shall duplicate as nearly as possible real life situations.

3. Motivation in learning is promoted by the understanding the learner has of the significance of the activities in which he is engaged and the satisfaction which they bring to him when completed.

4. A problem solving approach should be regarded as the best means for developing an understanding of the scientific methods and of the generalizations of science.

5. The application of generalizations to new situations should be an integral part of the learning procedure.

6. The application of methods used in problem solving in science should be made in new situations as an integral part of the learning procedure.

C. Objectives of secondary school science:

1. To provide exploratory experience for the acquisition of new fields of interest.

2. To develop a mastery of those knowledges which are functional in aiding the individual to adjust himself in a more satisfying manner to the world about him.

    3. To impart certain abilities to the student such as—
      a. Reliance on facts.
      b. Power of interpretation.
      c. Power of observation.
      d. Ability to evaluate data.
      e. Ability to think scientifically.
    4. To develop certain attitudes or traits in the learner such as—
      a. Objective attitude toward facts.
      b. Freedom from dogma and superstition.
      c. Tendency to hold conclusions as tentative and to suspend judgment until facts are secured.
      d. Willingness to revise one's opinions if the evidence warrants.
      e. Spirit of inquiry.
      f. Conviction of the universality of the cause and effect relationship.
    5. To develop an appreciation of the contribution of science to mankind.
  D. Criteria and principles for the selection of subject content and activities:
    1. Content should be selected which offers opportunities for students of varying interests and capacities.
    2. Content should build meaning and understanding for the generalizations of science which have the largest social implications.
    3. Content should be so varied that it provides ample exploratory experience in the knowledge and methods of thought and procedures of the major fields of science.
    4. Opportunities should be provided which afford students the means of judging and measuring their progress toward the objectives sought.
    5. Activities should be selected which provide opportunity for the exercise of the creative abilities of youth and for the joy, romance, and adventure that discovery and invention in science afford.
    6. In so far as possible, learning activities that call for direct, concrete, first-hand experiences should be selected.
    7. The courses on the various levels of secondary school science should consist of a series of physical and mental activities

that lead to those knowledges, skills, interests and attitudes essential to desirable mental and practical adjustments to the environment.

E. Organization of content and activities:
 1. The major divisions (units, topics, or problems) of the courses in secondary school science need to be organized so that the conceptions of science and their social implications once learned are used in new relationships in some later division.
 2. The content of courses in science should be organized to enable students to apply generalizations in the solving of new problems and the interpretation of novel phenomena.
 3. The organization of science content at all levels should stress the unity of science and avoid the development of unnatural distinction between fields.

F. Methods of instruction; *classroom* instruction:
 1. Methods of teaching should recognize varying degrees of ability on the part of students.
 2. Instruction should provide the learner with many opportunities to exercise important abilities in problem solving such as:
    a. Inferring causes from observed facts.
    b. Predicting effects from established causes.
    c. Divising hypotheses on the basis of observed phenomena.
    d. Analyzing data.
    e. Testing hypotheses by experiment.
    f. Reaching valid conclusions.
    g. Applying learned principles and facts in new situations.
 3. Science teachers on various levels of the secondary school need to recognize motivation as essential for learning and use devices to secure it in the classroom.
 4. Excursions into the local community to illustrate applications of knowledge, or for firsthand investigation, are desirable to promote learning.

G. Methods of instruction; *laboratory* instruction:
 1. Laboratory work in secondary school science should be designed to teach pupils how to observe, how to come to independent conclusions on the basis of their own observations, and how to check their conclusions.

2. Teachers of the various courses of secondary school science need to recognize that in some types of experimental situations effective learning is best obtained through the demonstration method, while in other situations the laboratory plan is superior.

3. The work of the classroom and laboratory should be closely correlated.

H. Evaluating learning products:

1. Factual tests are important only when the facts are essential to the attainment of more important objectives of instruction.

2. Tests should evaluate the student's progress in understanding the elementary generalizations of science.

3. Tests in science should evaluate, where possible, the student's progress in the development of various scientific attitudes.

4. Tests should reveal the student's ability to infer causes from observed effects and to predict effects from a given set of established causes.

5. Tests should provide evidence of the student's ability to apply learned elements in new situations and to draw valid conclusions from a given set of data.

I. Materials for instruction:

1. Visual aids should be regarded as valuable for vicarious experiences in the learning of science. They are of distinct value in preview and culminating activities for each learning unit.

2. It is essential for the teaching of science that equipment for teacher demonstrations and also for individual laboratory experimentation be provided.

Summary 1930–1940

The committees reporting in this decade took serious note of the past developments in science teaching, examined current practices and then sought to develop a consistent theory of education in science. For the first time, science curriculum committees were cognizant of learning theory as a factor in curriculum planning.

These curriculum groups were more influenced by the contemporary American scene and the growing importance of science and technology than were the committees in previous decades. How these factors should be represented in the science curriculum of the high school was widely debated. Essentially each committee felt that science was imperative in the education of young people for their intelligent understanding of the present society. This in turn led to a major emphasis upon science for all young people—meeting their "needs" and "problems"—and set the curriculum in terms of its values for personal and social welfare. This approach differed from that used by earlier committees in which the emphasis was more upon what is significant in terms of the subject or discipline.

The following ideas about science teaching in secondary schools were typical of the 1930–1940 decade.

1. Science teaching should contribute to the broader purposes of general education and must include content of wide personal and social significance.

2. Science is best learned as an association of facts culminating in a concept expressed as a principle or generalization of science. Facts acquired through a process of memorization have little value in "problem-solving" situations.

3. The skills, attitudes, and methods usually associated with the "problem-solving" aspect of scientific methodology are worthy objectives of science teaching. Most committees and much of the educational research of the period sought to "spell out" this aspect of the "scientific method."

4. The curriculum content is best defined in terms of the principles and generalizations of the subject field. This makes for a more adaptable curriculum and is consistent with the research on learning.

5. There should not be a distinction between class and laboratory procedures; both should contribute to the solution of problems.

6. Testing and evaluation should be in terms of *all* the objectives of the course. The best test is one that requires the student to apply his knowledge to novel situations.

7. There is need for a balanced program of science with some opportunity for all students to build a background in both the biological and physical sciences.

8. The program of science instruction should be continuous from the kindergarten through high school.

The reports of this period have been used more by curriculum specialists than by classroom teachers. The objectives listed in these reports, particularly those related to "scientific thinking" and "principles," became "standard" in lists of objectives for science teaching. Actually changes in classroom practices essential to a realization of the newer objectives did not materialize to any extent. On the other hand, the many research studies in science teaching stimulated by the reports of the 1930–1940 decade indicated that *it is* possible to develop skills in thinking, change attitudes, use principles as a focus of learning and that partial self-direction by students in the selection of learning problems is advantageous.

The committee reports of the period have been criticized for too much emphasis on *what* should be done in science teaching and too little on *how* it should be done, even though the major committees developed course outlines and sample teaching units to illustrate their points of view.

There were many doubts expressed during the Depression years about the values to be gained from a study of science in secondary schools. Too many courses were taught simply as a recitation of facts and definitions to be memorized and parroted back to the teacher. An examination of science tests showed that students were seldom asked to do more than "name parts," "give functions," "arrange in order" or "define terms." Each of the major curriculum committees of this period attempted to show that there was more to the study of science than this. The effort to define the curriculum content in terms of the broad principles of biology is an example of a technique used to focus courses on integrative concepts.

Most of the committees gave attention to the testing and evaluation of the more subtle aspects of science teaching such as the development of attitudes; the understanding of principles, concepts and generalizations; and the awareness and ability to use scientific procedures in solving problems of everyday living. Science teachers were being forced to demonstrate that they could teach something besides facts. Therefore new testing instruments became imperative.

The strongest criticism was leveled at the nature of individual student laboratory work and its lack of educational returns for the time spent. Extensive research was done on the values to be gained from individual laboratory work compared with the more economical teacher demonstration of the same material. These investigations showed that a student could accumulate "facts" by either procedure and that teacher demonstrations were more economical in time and money. (A summary of these research studies is presented in a later chapter of this book.) The net result was that the double or two-hour laboratory period in science teaching was dropped by the majority of high schools.

VII

Biology in General Education, 1940–1950

IN THE DECADE 1940–1950, World War II and the birth of the "atomic age" raised questions about the purposes of secondary school education as a whole and science teaching in particular. The movements in science education which began in the thirties were temporarily overshadowed by course adjustments made to meet "war time emergencies." New courses, such as pre-induction hygiene, aviation, electronics, and others were added to the secondary school curriculum. Biology teaching was not particularly affected by these developments, although there was a tendency to place more emphasis on hygiene, food and disease. The committee reports during the first part of the 1940–1950 period reflect movements which originated between 1930 and 1940 and those following World War II, represent attempts to reorient education in the sciences.

In 1940, a special committee of the American Council on Education issued a report on *What the High Schools Ought to Teach* (8). Various suggestions were made for a revision of the entire secondary school curriculum. The central recommendation called for a program of general education suitable for all students with some provision for specialized training.

The committee recognized the growing importance of science in education, but disapproved its present trend. "Courses in the natural sciences are now far too often mere encyclopedic lists of the findings of scientific research. They often fill the memory with facts rather than stimulate pupils to scientific thinking. Competent teachers here and there succeed in making these courses means of vital, effective thinking. When they achieve this purpose, and only then, do they fully justify the retention of courses in natural science in the curriculum."

In 1941, *The National Commission on Cooperative Curriculum Planning* was formulated with a membership representing the various disciplines and subject fields of the high school (61). This was an effort to look upon curriculum development in secondary schools as a whole, distinct from the previous patterns of considering each course separately. The question then becomes, what can instruction in science contribute to the over-all education of youth?

The commission recognized the distinctive function of science in the curriculum to be: 1) direct experience with the natural world through observation and experiment; 2) knowledge of the facts and laws of the natural world; and 3) an understanding of the ways in which knowledge of science can be applied. It is at this latter point that the line between science and the social sciences overlaps. The particular value of biology was regarded as "helping man to understand and control his environment," but taught in a way different from that of the social studies.

The practical applications of scientific knowledge to health practices, conservation, sanitation, consumership and other problems were regarded as the basis for defining courses. For example, science courses would be developed around problems, such as conservation, involving science, rather than around the separate subject fields. The science teacher would then draw upon physics, chemistry, geology, biology, and geography for needed materials of instruction, always determined by the nature of the problem.

It was thought that disciplines other than biology, physics and chemistry should be explored for their possible contribution to the general education in science. Especially should more time be devoted to understanding modern science, scientists as personalities and important experiments in each field.

The biological areas recommended for study included: 1) history of the past; 2) relation of man and his communities to the earth; 3) plants and animals and their classification; 4) the place of man among living things; 5) organic evolution; 6) heredity; 7) nutritional processes and nutritional relations among living things; 8) cycles of materials in the organic world; 9) plant and animal communities; 10) reproduction in plants and animals; 11) the human life cycle from conception to death; 12) general anatomy of the human body; 13) basic physiological functions; 14) internal adjustments of the body; 15) dietary needs of man; 16) nature and varieties of human disease and their control in the individual; 17) the nervous system, sense organs and sensations; 18) nature and methods of learning; 19) emotions and their place in human behavior; 20) individual differences—mental and physical; 21) mental and emotional conflicts and their control; 22) nature of knowledge (facts, generalizations, hypotheses, theories and how scientific knowledge changes).

The objectives of science in general education proposed by the Progressive Education Association were accepted, but with some changes in emphasis: 1) personal living (more on self-realization); 2) personal-social relationships (more on human relationships); 3) social-civic relationships (more on civic responsibilities); 4) economic relationships (more on economic efficiency).

The suggested curriculum was in accord with the trends in science teaching at this time, those of "effective consumership" and for ends that have a personal-social value to the student. Any modifications of the science curriculum would arise from changes in personal, social and economic problems, since science instruction must be oriented toward personal and social ends to be fully justified in the curriculum.

The commission felt that many science teachers were interested only in advancing the cause of science through the approach of a "zealous missionary" in teaching the subject. "They make sure of the perfected logical organization of a special brand of science and then try to teach it to as many students as possible, jealously guarding against any mention of the subject in other classes. If science is to have a place in general education, then it must broaden its perspectives, rather than seeking to remain vocational."

The following report is presented not so much for its findings but for its plan of attack on problems of secondary school science teaching. The *Bureau of Educational Research in Science,*

Teachers College, Columbia University, developed a plan to use scientists and educators jointly in working on the science curriculum (71). Scholars in science interpreted the major problems confronting society and then developed a series of volumes on the science background important to understanding these problems. "The preparation of these [reports] represents an effort to bring to curriculum committees in secondary schools a scholarly interpretation of some of the issues now under consideration in the dynamic secondary school curriculum and also reports on methods and results employed by successful teachers in dealing with these issues."

Cooperating high schools in several states tried out the new materials both for content and methods of teaching. Educators and scientists visited the high school teachers and the teachers visited each other to work out better techniques of presenting materials and to assist in curriculum development.

In 1942, a committee with representatives from seventeen scientific and science teaching societies met to develop "a philosophy or point of view" for instruction in secondary school science (62). Replies from 2,500 science teachers to a questionnaire were considered in developing the final report. High school science teachers and administrators worked as consultants to the committee on various phases of the study.

A summary of the report follows:

A. Points of view on the teaching of science:
   1. Science teaching should focus on *better living* in our society.
   2. The greatest contribution of the scientist to better living is his method and it should be applied to personal and social problems.
   3. The modern world is the product of science but there is a need to further increased confidence in science.
   4. Science teaching should stress problems of everyday living including social problems involving science. There is a need to relate the basic principles of science to the culture in which we live, with less emphasis on memorizing, formally organized subject matter, and performing technical laboratory exercises.

    5. Science teaching should ultimately lead to:
      a. A science for human betterment.
      b. A development of a broader outlook for pupils.
      c. A betterment of community living.
      d. An application of the scientific method to social-economic ills.
      e. A concern with the "wholeness" of problems of modern living.
      f. A concern with the needs of students, rather than organized bodies of facts.
      g. A greater understanding of the democratic way of life.
      h. A willingness to explore controversial issues, such as sex instruction, control of patents for the common good, and others.

B. Selection of instructional materials for courses:
    1. There should be sufficient knowledge taught to develop an understanding of science and of those engaged in scientific pursuits; to use intelligently the benefits of science in everyday living; and to solve problems of personal and social significance.
    2. There should be an emphasis upon problems arising in the local situation.
    3. There should be a recognition of different maturity levels among students and a differentiation between courses for college and non-college students.

C. Classroom procedures:
    1. The work of the class should be developed in terms of problems requiring the use of scientific methods, scientific attitudes and critical thinking for their solution.
    2. Visual aids, laboratory experiments, demonstrations, and reference books should be regarded as sources of data for the classroom study of problems.

The committee throughout its report gave strong support to the social functions of science and the importance of providing the kind of education that will help individuals live effectively in a scientifically oriented world. It was emphasized, however, that the goals of the scientists for extending knowledge are not the same as the goals of education in science.

Redirecting Science Teaching in the Light of Personal-Social Needs is a report of the *National Committee on Science Teaching,* published in 1942 (27). The membership of the committee was selected from the American Council of Science Teachers, American Association for the Advancement of Science, American Chemical Society, American Nature Study Society, American Science Teachers Association, Association of Science Teachers of the Middle States, Central Association of Science and Mathematics Teachers, National Association of Biology Teachers, National Association for Research in Science Teaching, National Council on Elementary Science, The American Association of Physics Teachers, and the National Council of Geography Teachers; the last two organizations "selected representatives to attend some meetings but did not officially vote to cooperate with the Committee." Eighty-five science teachers, school administrators and college teachers of science served as consultants. In addition, replies from 2,500 science teachers to a questionnaire were considered.

The committee's purpose was "to explore needs as a basis for redirecting science teaching." The following recommendations were developed.

A. Theory of science education:
 1. The place of science in schools is dependent upon the achievements of science and the contributions science can make to better living; the role of science in human affairs is central to education.
 2. Science teaching should serve the needs of pupils in our democratic society. "Needs are conceived here as desirable directions of growth and reasonable achievements, at the individual's level of development, which make for his welfare and that of our society. Most needs are at the same time both personal and social."
B. Aims and objectives of science teaching:
 1. The emphasis is *not* on objectives stated in terms of scientific generalizations but in terms of the personal-social needs of individuals.
 2. The following areas of needs are likely to be among those

common to a majority of students and toward which science teaching can contribute:
  a. Health
  b. Safety
  c. Recreation
  d. Maturing interpersonal relationships
  e. Work
  f. Intelligent consumership
  g. Conservation
  h. Maturing philosophy of life
  i. Responsible socio-economic action
  3. The scientific method and the scientific attitudes are seen as necessary to make all areas of needs functional.
C. Organization of courses:
  1. Courses should be planned in terms of broad, purposeful, experience units, to offer a better opportunity for exploring and meeting student needs.
  2. The content of units should cut across subject matter lines as necessary. The work in science should not be classified by courses or subjects, but as outcomes of science teaching or the common goals of general education.
  3. Courses should be organized around "problems"; the logical organization of the discipline is secondary.
  4. The "unified" curriculum the "core" curriculum, and the "broad-field" courses are best suited for developing courses centered around problems of living.

In brief, this committee felt that objectives should be stated in "functional" terms rather than around the principles of science. Accordingly, student "needs" were regarded as the best approach to curriculum development. A program of science teaching, from kindergarten through the junior college, based upon "functional outcomes" was outlined by the committee to serve as a guide for the reorganization of science programs in local schools.

In 1942, the *Committee on the Teaching of Biology* of the Union of American Biological Societies published the results of a questionnaire survey on high school biology teaching in the United States (76). The major purpose of the study was to ascertain the status of biology instruction in high schools. The findings from the questionnaire with regard to biology curriculum showed that of 3,186 biology teachers:

A. About 75% of the teachers were satisfied with the biology textbooks they were using. The degree of satisfaction was closely related to the opportunity for choosing one's own text.
B. Less than half of the teachers taught organic evolution; one-fifth did not teach the genetic inequality of man; and one-third did not consider sex education. The percentages varied for each topic according to the size of the school, and whether the school was public, parochial or private.
C. The teachers felt that the *greatest* emphasis in general biology should be on:
    1. Health—disease—hygiene
    2. Physiology
    3. Heredity
    4. Conservation
    5. Structure
D. The teachers gave the *lowest* rating (in terms of emphasis) to the following topics:
    1. Eugenics
    2. Behavior
    3. Scientific method
    4. Photosynthesis
    5. Biological principles

A conclusion of the committee was that there is a tendency "to teach biology not as a science, but (a) as a way to pleasing hobbies, or (b) as a series of practical technologies."

The Cooperative Committee on Science Teaching, representing the American Association of Physics Teachers, American Chemical Society, Mathematical Association of America, Union of American Biological Societies, and the National Association for Research in Science Teaching, reported in 1943 on proposed changes in the science curriculum to help increase manpower during the World War II period (39). There were no major changes recommended for either biology or chemistry, but in case a cut back in science offerings became necessary in the high school, biology was to be retained.

The committee felt that the wartime values to be obtained from a study of biology were:

1. A rational view of living things.
2. A knowledge of nutrition and personal hygiene.
3. A basic knowledge of agriculture and animal husbandry.
4. A prerequisite and a stimulus to enter medicine, public health service, teaching, research and agriculture.

The course in high school biology should emphasize the following topics:

1. Human body; structure, function, care, first aid and nutrition.
2. Bacteria and disease.
3. Personal and public health.
4. Use of plant products; food, shelter, medicine, clothing and others.
5. Genetics; plant and animal breeding.
6. Conservation; soil, forests, grasslands, wildlife and flood control.
7. Applied ecology.

Special attention needs to be given to victory-gardens and the raising of medicinal plants.

The *Educational Policies Commission* of the National Education Association in 1944 issued a report, *Education for All American Youth* (33). This report was developed from a firm conviction on the part of the *Educational Policies Commission* that the extension, adaptation, and improvement of secondary education is essential both to the security of our American institutions and to the economic well-being of our people. The report represented three years of study during which time the commission developed a statement of general principles with suggestions for bringing these into school practice. The commission foresaw demands for a change in the nature of secondary education and were inclined to believe that the nature and direction of change could be controlled. It supported the premise that an educational program developed at the local and state level was more acceptable than a federalized system of education.

Secondary education from the commission's point of view should: 1) develop a broad and balanced education for all which would equip each youth to enter an occupation suited to his abilities and would offer reasonable opportunities for personal growth and social usefulness; 2) prepare youth to assume their full responsibilities of American citizenship and provide each with a fair chance to exercise his right to happiness; 3) stimulate intellectual curiosity and engender satisfaction with intellectual achievement; 4) cultivate the ability to think rationally; and 5) help develop an appreciation of ethical values.

Science instruction in particular was recognized as "one of the chief elements in the cultural heritage; and the understanding of scientific methods and the scientific point of view as a part of the cultural birthright of youth." Thus it was recommended that: 1) science instruction should begin in the first grade and continue throughout the secondary school; 2) not only the scientific facts should be taught but also the methods by which these facts were discovered; there is a real danger that pupils may learn to take science on the authority of the textbook and the teacher and fail to develop the attitude of critical inquiry which marks the scientific mind; 3) students should practice scientific inquiry to develop a knowledge of the experimental method, an understanding of the nature of truth and a respect for truth arrived at by rational processes; and 4) students should be stimulated to approve the way in which science has influenced man's way of living and thinking.

It was suggested that a considerable part of the tenth grade science course should be devoted to the role of science in human progress, and a course on "the scientific view of the world and of man" was defined. This course would include an imaginative association with great scientists, the study of the history of science and its dramatic action. The methods of science, accordingly, would be taught as instruments by which some of humanity's most important problems may be solved. Certainly some of the great experiments of recent years as well as the more remote ones should be studied.

The cultural outcomes expected from the teaching of science were stated as follows: 1) "An educated person will understand that science is based upon methods which man must slowly and painstakingly develop for discovering, verifying, interpreting and organizing the facts of the world in which we live and about the people in it." 2) "He will know that the use of scientific methods has made revolutionary changes in man's way of living and thinking." 3) "He will see that the methods of science are one of mankind's chief instruments for making further progress." 4) "He will know that scientific advances have depended upon precise measurement and active calculations; that mathematics is indispensable to scientific inquiry." 5) "He will recognize that problems in human society as well as in the physical world should be attacked by scientific methods and a scientific point of view." 6) "He will be familiar with certain fundamental principles and facts of the sciences, which, when taken together, give him a sound view of the nature of the world in which he lives." A student who does not understand the social nature of science is living in the 15th century, no matter how many facts he can recite or how many scientific gadgets he can operate.

The commission felt that a high school curriculum should include a course in "common learnings" and that ideally science would be an integral part of the content. It recognized, however, that there was not an adequate supply of teachers qualified to teach science in relation to the other phases of the common-learnings. At that time, therefore, it seemed advisable to include a separate basic course in science in grade ten. This course would be closely related to the work in "common learning" and would be planned cooperatively with the teachers of "common learnings."

A basic course in science was recommended for all high school students. Although the courses for rural and city youth would differ in some respects, the major aim for both courses should be an understanding of the social significance of science: one of the ten imperative educational needs of youth. The basic course was described as "The Scientific View of the World and of Man." In the farm areas the social applications would include enlightening rural communities (for example, soil conservation, electrification) but would not consist exclusively of practical applications. In the cities, comparable attention would be given to the effect of urban life on industry; the improvement of housing, transportation, home and neighborhood life along with the application of scientific knowledge to the planning and development of cities.

In actuality science was given a minor place in the secondary school curriculum. Only one course, essentially the sociology of science, was suggested for the high school. The scientists' reactions to the program were that the course presented something *about* science but there was little that in reality could be called science. The scientists disagreed not so much with the course objectives but with the methods to be used for a realization of them. They did not feel that an understanding of the methodology of science could be developed through attempts to apply the procedures to social problems.

The Place of Science in the Education of the Consumer was a statement prepared for the Consumer Education Society of the National Association of Secondary School Principals by the *National Science Teachers Association* in 1945 (69). The Consumer Education Society assumed that the intelligent consumer was the immediate objective of secondary school education, and that "any science worth teaching for any reason has value in the education of consumers." In a society characterized by a scientific, industrial technology and a complex exchange economy, the contribution of science to education is one of providing information about goods and services, and the development of critical thinking necessary to the best use of such information. Science teaching should therefore focus on knowledge which helps consumers purchase wisely and on procedures useful in the solution of consumer problems.

Content for a science course should be selected in terms of activities which account for a high proportion of consumer expenditures and especially those of immediate importance to young people. Among the problem areas to be included in science instruction were: 1) nutritional problems; the preparation of foods, sanitation; 2) standards by which to procure foods; 3) housing; kinds and qualities of material, household maintenance and operation; 4) clothing; buying and standards; 5) health; wiser buying of remedies and health services, the avoidance of worthless drugs and devices, and dangers of self medication; 6) standardization; labelling, and advertising regulations; 7) conserving natural resources.

The committee pointed out that: biology, physics, chemistry and other established courses in the secondary school could be given a definite consumer education slant; this would be a simpler arrangement than the development of special courses. Furthermore, laboratory exercises, surveys of the community, the use of special family problems and consumer clubs provide effective ways of presenting consumer information. The teacher of science should possess a comprehensive understanding of science, technology, economics, and society to qualify him for consumer teaching.

In 1944 a committee representing the National Association of Secondary School Principals recommended a program of education for youth between the ages of 16 and 21 years. (59) It was suggested that a single course in science, "the scientific view of the world and man," be required of all students in the tenth grade. The special sciences, biology, chemistry and physics, would all be elective courses.

The statement of objectives for teaching science was similar to those found in *Education for All American Youth*. Essentially science was viewed as a subject where the student learns how to use the fruits of science in daily living and to exert control over the physical and biological environment. The committee suggested that these ends were best achieved through: 1) a knowledge of the facts and principles of science; and 2) an understanding of the methods of science. It was assumed that the methods of science can be used to resolve social problems in the same manner as problems in science.

General Education in a Free Society is the report of the *Harvard University Committee on General Education* (73). Its purpose was to define the objectives of "general education in a free society" not only for Harvard College but for schools in general. Only those sections of the report which bear upon the teaching of science are summarized here.

1. Point of view on science in general education:
   a. "Science instruction in general education should be characterized mainly by broad integrative elements—the comparison of scientific with other modes of thought, the comparison and contrast of the individual sciences with one another, the relations of science with its own past and with general human history, and of science with the problems of human society." These are areas in which science can make a lasting contribution to the general education of all students.
   b. Science courses should convey some familiarity with the world of immediate experience. "The integrative element here is the student's own mode of life and his personal relation to the immediate environment."
   c. "The facts of science and the experiences of the laboratory no longer can stand by themselves, they no longer represent simple, spontaneous, and practical elements directly related to the daily life of the student. As they become further removed from his experience, more subtle, more abstract, the facts must be learned in another context, cultural, historical and philosophical. Only such broader perspectives can give point and lasting value to scientific information and experience for the general student."
   d. Below college level, virtually all science should be devoted to general education. Even vocational instruction should retain elements of the scientific attitudes.
   e. Direct observation and precision are among the most important values along with basic ideas that science should contribute to general education. Laboratory work therefore is essential to science teaching in order to provide directly the materials of scientific argument and the tests of scientific hypothesis.
   f. Scientific methods should not be used upon materials wholly

unsuited to their use. Modes of inquiry must be adapted to materials under consideration and to the available methods of approach.

g. There is need in high school to offer a rigorous and highly integrated introduction to science as a whole.

h. Science courses in high school need to go beyond the immediate environment and start to segregate for the student the differences in the point of view and approach which divide sciences into separate disciplines. The student should be introduced to the techniques, the major science concepts, and the hypotheses appropriate to each science.

i. "Science is not to be divorced from technology. Science and technology develop in parallel, each fructifying the other. Yet science is not technology. Its prime end is knowing rather than doing, or better still, it is doing in order that one may know, rather than doing with primarily other ends in view—greater convenience, technical efficiency, military power, or economic advantage, for example."

2. Sequence of courses and organization:

   a. Ninth and tenth grades: biology

     (1) A considerable part of biology should be a study of the works of great biologists.

     (2) Part of the course needs to be organized into projects involving laboratory or field experiences which parallel the work of the classroom.

   b. Eleventh and twelfth grades: physics and chemistry

     (1) Physics and chemistry should be taken only by those primarily interested in college.

     (2) A better course for general education at this level would be a course in physical science—a broad view of the nature and organization of the physical world and a more mature approach to the related scientific concepts.

The Harvard Committee, in contrast to several other committees of this period, does not regard the "scientific method" as applicable to all types of problems. The methods of science should not be used ". . . upon material wholly unsuited to whatever methods may be employed under that guise; and more realization that statements in the literary or social sphere necessarily are different in nature, and in precision, from statements in mechanics." The scientific attitudes are recognized as having a more general value. The committee believes the facts of science should be given a broader perspective and placed in a cultural, historical and philosophical context. The science teacher was seen as a student of both science and of the liberal arts.

The Teaching of the Basic Sciences (44) is the report of a committee formulated in 1943 at the request of the United States Commissioner of Education, J. W. Studebaker, to "canvass carefully the question of whether the basic sciences should not be included along with vocational education in a federally subsidized program. Such a subsidization would include, of course, the appropriate training of teachers for such courses."

The situation in science teaching was summarized as follows:

1. There is a conspicuous lack of training in the physical sciences in the secondary school; a larger number are enrolled in the biological sciences.
2. Half of our schools have six or fewer teachers and under the present licensing and certification system most of the schools cannot afford to hire a teacher for the physical sciences.
3. Some of the best science teaching in smaller high schools is carried on by the teachers of agriculture particularly in states where the time of such teachers is pro-rated and they do not spend all of their time in vocational agriculture.
4. Those now teaching science in the high school are, in many states, poorly prepared in their respective subjects, being on the whole measurably less well prepared than trainees in the same field for industry.
5. Because only a small proportion of high school students take science, science teachers must teach other subjects. Many teach three, four, or even more subjects which may be almost entirely unrelated. Science teaching is also assigned to individuals who are mainly interested in some other subject and had science as only a minor subject in college.
6. The situation could be remedied by certification of science teachers in comprehensive areas, such as a combination of the physical sciences with the biological sciences, or of the physical sciences with mathematics and geography.

7. It is necessary to realize that teachers trained in comprehensive science areas are also potential candidates for industrial positions, since the starting salary and life expectancy of earnings are far higher in industry than in the schools.

The committee recognized that while the public in general regrets extension of Federal aid to education, it seems that Federal aid of some kind will be necessary to strengthen the teaching of the basic sciences.

An expansion of the present vocational-technical education program to include science teaching is recommended. The ideas advocated were:

1. Improvement of basic preparation in science and mathematics for science teachers.
2. Improvement of the instruction in science for students not planning to enter vocational-technical programs.
3. Establishment of a unified, properly supported program in vocational-technical education including mathematics and sciences that are elements therein.
4. Encouragement of the development of a technical-institute type of training at the post-high school level, properly differentiated from the professional programs offered by engineering schools.

The President's Scientific Research Board in its report on *Science and Public Policy* made extensive recommendations for science teaching in the elementary and secondary schools (79). The following problems were first identified:

1. Elementary science concepts are introduced with little recognition of sequence from grade to grade and without correlation. Even in cases where the program has been effectively planned the teachers often lack a complete awareness of the goals and the procedures necessary to achieve them. Grade placement of concepts is prompted by tradition and teachers' preferences rather than by any systematic selection.
2. The majority of youth is exposed to general sciences and life sciences in some form; only a small fraction is encouraged to study physical science. Even the minority which goes on to

college may graduate and yet remain scientifically illiterate—
so inadequate is the science requirement for the general student. Then again, the science specialist may go through college
without becoming aware of the social implications of science.
3. Programs for the educational guidance of students identified
   as scientifically able are inadequate.
4. The professional training of scientists is often so specialized
   that technicians rather than scientists are produced.

Among the committee's recommendations for *immediate* action were:

1. Federal subsidized scholarships for gifted students in all fields.
2. The establishment of in-service teacher training programs
   through the use of workshops or science counselors or both.

Recommendations for a *long-range* program were:

1. Sponsor investigations of grade and age placement of science
   concepts to improve curriculum planning.
2. Promote the designing of testing instruments and guidance
   procedures to assist in the early identification of the talented.
3. Stimulate the widespread use of cumulative student records
   to include elementary, secondary and college education.
4. Provide information on guidance procedures free of charge
   to all school systems throughout the country.

It was felt that all youth should have an understanding of:
1) the methods of science; 2) the influence of science upon human
life and thought; 3) the facts and principles essential to an understanding of themselves and of their environment; and 4) an
appreciation of the scientific enterprise. Science instruction
should also contribute to the social adjustment of young people
through the use of its methods and findings in the solution of
problems.

The committee then considered the special problems of science
teaching at the elementary and secondary school levels. In the
elementary school the following problems caused concern: 1) the
incidental nature of science teaching in elementary schools; 2)
the attempts to teach elementary science in conjunction with so-

cial studies; 3) the lack of science training among elementary teachers; 4) the great variety of subject matter in elementary courses; 5) the lack of any clear-cut indication as to how one concept should follow another for the best learning; 6) the lack of equipment for the teaching of elementary science; 7) the extent of verbal descriptions without adequate contact with the real things of science.

The function of science in elementary schools was seen as: 1) understanding the environment through contact with the problems inherent in the physical and biological surroundings; 2) developing of some understanding of the elements of the scientific method and facility in problem solving, embodying observation, experimenting and reflective thinking; 3) developing an understanding of the social implications of science; and 4) acquiring something of the scientific attitudes. The committee felt "elementary science should provide special educational opportunities for potential scientists." It recognized the need for more research in the field of elementary school science, particularly on: 1) the concepts, principles and skills of science which may be taught in the elementary school and the study of the appropriate time allotments; 2) appropriate facilities, equipment and teaching materials; 3) the use of the local environment including trips afield; 4) procedures for integrating science concepts with mathematics; and 5) ways of teaching pupils to use a "scientific" approach in problematic situations.

Science in the secondary school curriculum must continue to serve the same functions as elementary school science; namely, contribute to the general education of all students and the special education of a selected group.

The committee recognized the changing nature of the high school and the need to introduce science courses to meet new general education needs. Concern was expressed about the low enrollment in the physical sciences and the inappropriateness of much of the content of the present physics and chemistry courses for purposes of general education. "Observation would indicate that many who are enrolled might better be served by a general course in physical science . . ." Additional work in the biological sciences beyond the first course should be offered to provide an opportunity for those students with special interests. It was recommended that special provision should be made for and recognition given to the mentally gifted students through honors classes, science fairs, science congresses, specialized science courses, special projects, club activities, or combinations of these plans.

The importance of laboratory work with experience in observation and experimentation was regarded as self-evident in science teaching. Both demonstration experiments and individual work can be used to achieve many of the objectives of science teaching. Experimentation develops skills and coordination in manipulation; trains the powers of observation; and provides opportunities for developing resourcefulness in the use of physical materials and instruments. Individual laboratory work with its active participation is to be desired over passive observation.

The following recommendations were made for the improvement of secondary school science teaching:

1. A complete appraisal should be made of science teaching in secondary schools, including a survey of curriculum, student enrollment, available laboratory and demonstration equipment, methods of instruction, work week of teachers, and preparation of teachers for their responsibilities.
2. The secondary school science curriculum should be reorganized so as to permit at least two years of science beyond general science for all students—general biology and general physical science—and at least three years of science for students with special talents in science and mathematics—botany, zoology, physics and chemistry or other special courses. Studies should be made of the effectiveness of the present high school science offerings with a view of designing new courses.
3. A study should be made of the place, value and effective use of biographical and historical materials in high school science courses.
4. A study should be made of the various curricula and administrative arrangements employed in small and large com-

munities to meet the needs of talented youths and reports should be prepared to inform science teachers of the best practices.

5. An investigation should be made of the guidance procedures used in secondary schools, including studies of aptitude tests, criteria for the identification of the talented, and the follow-up procedures.

6. Studies should be made to determine the most effective use of illustrative material, laboratory projects, field experiences, library materials, and audio-visual aids in the teaching of science.

7. Studies should be made of the administrative devices which will encourage greater use of community resources in the teaching of science.

8. The activities of science supervisors, special consultants, visiting teachers, and other special advisory personnel should be studied with a view to making their use more prevalent.

The committee noted that there was at that time (1947) a serious shortage of secondary school science and mathematics teachers. One of the contributing factors had been low salaries; "numerous studies indicate, however, there are sections of this country without sufficient local or state resources to maintain an adequate system of education. This indicates the need to make Federal funds available for equalizing educational opportunity."

The conditions under which science teachers were required to work, both administrative and physical, were found to be appalling: the large demands on the science teachers' time through the preparation of demonstration and laboratory experiments, after-school clubs, and many other non-teaching activities.

The training of elementary school teachers in science was particularly lacking. It was suggested the teachers' college initiate studies to determine the kind of science courses most suitable for elementary school science teachers. It was also recommended that the curriculum for the prospective teacher of elementary science include a minimum of six semester hours of biological science and six semester hours of physical science, both with professionalized laboratory and field work. If the professionalized laboratory and field work cannot be provided, an additional two-

or three-semester-hour course in elementary science methods should be required. This would be taught by a person familiar, through training or experience, with the problems of the elementary school. The committee recommended the increase of in-service programs to improve instruction.

The training of secondary school science teachers was seen by the committee to be something less than desirable. A major problem was the untrained person teaching on an emergency permit; the exact number in this category could not be determined. The committee noted also that undergraduate courses in science are more often intended for people who are to become specialists in science; such courses fail to give breadth of understanding or comprehension of the interrelationship existing among the many specialized fields of science and mathematics, an understanding essential for teachers in the secondary schools. "The undergraduate training program for teachers of science and mathematics, to be most effective, must be a specifically planned, professionalized program."

The many and varied subject combinations that science teachers are required to teach seriously limits their effectiveness. A typical situation: in a study of 3,490 teachers in 525 public four-year accredited secondary schools in Illinois, a total of 716 different subject combinations were found. "Of 293 teachers of biology only 3.4% were teaching biology and one other subject, 38% were teaching biology and two other subjects and 19% three other subjects. These teachers were assigned to a total of 124 different combinations and were teaching 25 subjects in addition to biology."

The Steelman Committee accepted and supported a series of proposals, prepared by the American Association for the Advancement of Science Cooperative Committee on The Preparation of High School Science and Mathematics Teachers, for the guidance of college and university curriculum committees on teacher education. Some of the recommendations of the committee were:

1. "A policy of certification in closely related subjects within the broad area of science and mathematics should be established

and put into practice. Specifically any combination of three of the following five subjects is recommended: biological science (including botany and zoology), chemistry, mathematics, physics and general science.

2. "Additional courses permitting the student to complete a total of 24 should be given to courses in science and mathematics. Sixty semester hours, divided among three subjects will allow for a 24-hour major in one science subject and 18 hours in each of two others.

3. "Certification to teach general science at the 7th, 8th, or 9th grade level should be granted on the basis of broad preparation including college courses in all the subjects concerned in general science."

The committee "further recommended that a basic program of 6 to 10 semester hours in each of the beginning courses in biology, chemistry, mathematics, and physics be required. In addition to the basic program 18 to 24 semester hours in 2 or 3 of the special subjects should be required."

"Professionalized subject matter courses should be planned cooperatively by the subject matter and education departments and taught by persons with experience in teaching the particular subject matter in the secondary school. It is not meant to be implied that those showing a high degree of proficiency in subject matter are automatically destined to be good teachers. But, obviously, strong aptitude in subject matter, plus professional skill, good personality, and a genuine interest in young people, should be expected to comprise the best in science and mathematics teaching in the secondary school." The problem of training future science teachers is a matter in which the university should have a special interest.

The committee supported the desirability of in-service education at the secondary level. "Plans should be developed for using curriculum workshops, institutes, extra-mural content courses, summer school instruction, demonstrations, lectures, field trips, excursions and conferences for the training of secondary school science and mathematics teachers. Plans for the further education of teachers after they have been in service have not been systematically organized to serve the needs of this group. The graduate offerings in science and mathematics are usually too highly specialized and narrowly defined to serve the needs of any individual who does not intend to become a research scientist. Some teacher training institutions should provide for at least one year of graduate work in which ample courses in science and mathematics are offered to meet the needs of the teacher instead of the research scientist."

Science Education in American Schools (1947) is the Forty-Sixth Yearbook, Part I, of the National Society for the Study of Education (64). This yearbook contains the deliberations of several committees selected to develop a challenging and workable philosophy of science teaching, to consider new kinds of courses, and to explore methods of science instruction. The viewpoints developed and the recommendations made were:

1. Viewpoints on science instruction:
    a. Science is an inescapable factor in modern society which in turn requires that everyone understand science.
    b. "We must improve our general education by including convincing and effective personal and community controls of knowledge. Merely factual education might have only harmful results for future peoples."
    c. "... if the people's representatives, who pass legislation, are to make decisions for an age of science, they need at least a reasonable knowledge of science and her ways of working. The ways of thinking of the politician and of the scientist have differed widely. Each group needs to understand and cooperate with the other. And the common man, if not a scientist, nonetheless needs knowledge of both science and legislation since both profoundly affect his welfare."
    d. "Science now bears a definite relationship to many kinds of social standards, and social standards are influential in people's conduct."
    e. Science instruction should begin early in the experience of the child.
    f. The program of science teaching for both the elementary and secondary schools should contribute mainly to general education.

g. Competence in use of the scientific method of problem solving and the inculcation of scientific attitudes are the major goals of science teaching.

2. The learning of science:
   a. Functional understanding is more than memorizing; it is the ability to use or apply knowledge dependent upon the conscious effort of both teachers and student "to make the proper connections."
   b. The more artificial the learning situation the more artificial the learning.
   c. "Facts, concepts, and principles are functional only if they are actually used. We learn to use them effectively by *using* them and in no other way."

3. The objectives of science teaching:
   a. The following criteria should guide the formulation of teaching objectives:
      (1) *Practicable*—for the classroom teacher and when used properly should lead logically from one step to another.
      (2) *Psychologically sound*—based on acceptable principles of learning.
      (3) *Possible of attainment*—under reasonably favorable circumstances with an average group of pupils.
      (4) *Universal in a democratic society.*
      (5) *Indicate the relationship of classroom activity* to *desired changes in human behavior.*
   b. The general objectives of science teaching:
      (1) Functional information.
      (2) Functional concepts.
      (3) Functional understanding of principles.
      (4) Instrumental skills—making accurate measurements, etc.
      (5) Problem solving skills.
      (6) Attitudes—open-mindedness, etc.
      (7) Appreciations—cause and effect relationships, contributions of scientists, etc.
      (8) Interests—recreational and vocational.
   c. Each of the objectives should be interwoven with its social implications.
   d. Objectives are conceived as directions of growth rather than outcomes.

4. Criteria for the selection of subject matter:
   a. Science content should be selected in terms of problems of social significance as they relate to the broad areas of human experience such as health, consumership, conservation, vocations, family relationships, and citizenship.
   b. Subject matter should relate to the problems encountered in daily living and meet the real needs of students.
   c. Subject matter should be selected to take advantage of community resources wherever possible.
   d. Subject matter should be selected for its functional value and the contribution it can make to the understanding of the principles and generalizations of science.
   e. It is assumed that all learning should contribute to scientific attitudes, the use of scientific methods and toward developing a philosophy of life.
   f. The course content shall be of a proper degree of difficulty in relation to the maturity level of the pupils.
   g. Content which appeals to pupil interest is more likely to influence his behavior than that which is not.
5. Organization of science courses:
   a. The courses in science should be organized around significant problems, based upon the principles and generalizations of science around wider problems of adjustment involving these principles and generalizations.
   b. "One method that has value in several directions is that of planning the course with the pupils instead of merely for them."
   c. Attempts should be made to organize the course in order to develop an integration of the various sciences and of principles within the same science. A logical sequence within a science is not of itself a primary goal.
   d. Courses should be organized to provide for wide applications to economic and social problems.
6. Classroom teaching procedures:
   a. Members of the class should be working together and full advantage should be taken of group discussion.
   b. Report on current science events and articles, especially in newspapers and magazines, provide an opportunity for critical thinking in science.

c. Personal and community needs provide an opportunity for individual and group projects.

d. Field trips and excursions have value, particularly if taken for a recognized purpose.

e. Textbook, magazines, bibliographies, and other reference books should be available, preferably in the classroom.

f. Materials should be visualized whenever possible instead of being allowed to remain as abstract ideas. A wide variety of multi-sensory aids is desirable.

g. Inductive and deductive methods of teaching are equally important and essential in the classroom. Several approaches are not only desirable but necessary.

h. The textbook is best used as a general outline of the course but needs to be supplemented with a variety of references.

i. Units of work should be planned around an integrating theme.

j. The stress should be on a few units well taught rather than on many units surveyed.

k. Whatever methods are used, they should contribute to the development of habits of thinking, attitudes, and appreciations.

7. Laboratory teaching procedures:

a. The laboratory work should be a phase of the classroom work, performed when necessary.

b. "... the inductive method should in nearly all cases be used; that is, the laboratory work should precede, not follow, the classroom discussion of a topic or a principle."

c. "In the interests of economy of both time and money, it is desirable to perform more laboratory exercises by the demonstration than by the individual method."

d. "At the start of every laboratory course there should be a sufficient use of the demonstration method to acquaint the pupils with accepted methods of experimentation."

e. Individual experiments should be done when it is a question of developing manipulatory skills and laboratory techniques and habits.

f. If an exercise is worth performing, it is worth recording for the following reasons: to direct the pupils' attention, establish habits of looking for details, and reinforce memory.

g. The student should develop, with the teacher's help, the procedures to be used in an experiment. The student should rely on his own findings, recognizing that accuracy is within the limitations of the apparatus and his own skill.

h. The laboratory work should be constructed to teach pupils the meaning and use of controls in experimentation, the testing of hypotheses and the interpretation of data.

i. Workbooks, provided they are well-constructed (not a series of completion questions), save the teacher's time and energy and provide the student with a wide range of learning activities.

8. Testing and evaluation:

a. Evaluation should be regarded as an integral part of the total instructional process.

b. Guidance of learning discloses the essential function of evaluation. Evaluation "provides data by means of which to determine initial status or readiness for learning, progress and difficulties in learning, final attainment, and extent of retention and transfer."

c. Principles of evaluation:

(1) It "must begin with a consideration of the outcome sought."

(2) It "must be comprehensive enough to include *all* outcomes and not merely those outcomes in which learning is most easily assessed" such as, factual knowledge and mechanical skills.

(3) "The procedures and devices employed in evaluation must also be comprehensive, for no single procedure is adequate to the task of furnishing to the teacher all the data needed for a complete picture of learning."

d. Tests should provide evidence of the science concepts developed in the course rather than simply the acquisition of factual knowledge.

9. Sequence of courses:

a. A twelve-year sequence of science courses is recommended as follows:

Grades I–VI—Elementary science
Grades VII–IX—General Science
Grade X—Biology
Grade XI—Physics or chemistry
Grade XII—Physics or chemistry

b. An integrated course in general biology and general physical science is also recommended for the high school, but the physical science course is not to replace physics and chemistry.

c. The attitude of the committee toward aeronautics, physiology, health, consumer and technical courses is that "it is probably not desirable to offer separate courses in any of these subjects . . . integrate materials with those of the regular courses."

d. An adequate program of science in a core curriculum is worthy of experiment, but not as these courses are usually taught by English and social studies teachers.

This committee has placed a greater emphasis upon class and laboratory techniques than have previous committees, and more emphasis upon the social implications of science. Objectives are regarded as directions of growth rather than as outcomes, and units of work are planned as areas of experience rather than as areas of knowledge.

The *Cooperative Committee on the Effectiveness of Science Teaching* of the American Association for the Advancement of Science reported, in 1948, its recommendations and observations for the improvement of science in education (45).

1. With regard to curriculum:
   a. The science offerings should be planned as a continuous program from grade one through twelve.
   b. "Every effort must be made to introduce systematically the concepts and ideas of science which the *average* citizen needs to understand."
   c. Gifted students should have special opportunities to develop their talents.
   d. There needs to be a better integration of science and mathematical concepts.
   e. "Interest in the physical sciences suffers a great deal because their relation to the neighboring sciences, such as biology, astronomy, and geology is not enough emphasized either on the high school or college level."
   f. Because biology is the only contact with science for so many high school students more attention should be given in the course to "the tactics and strategy of science."
   g. The committee was shocked to learn that the subject of evolution is not permitted in many schools.

2. With regard to teacher education:
   a. There is need to design a curriculum that is appropriate for training teachers of science.
   b. Teachers of science need to be trained in the broad areas of science rather than highly specialized.
3. With regard to research in science education:
   a. Comprehensive studies should be undertaken to determine the concepts and principles of science essential to an adequate program of general education.
   b. Experimental data are needed to aid teachers in planning an effective grade and age placement for the teaching of science concepts.
   c. A detailed study of methods for the early identification and guidance of science talent at all school levels should be undertaken.

In 1941, the *Cooperative Committee on Science Teaching* was established with representatives from five scientific societies—biology, chemistry, mathematics, physics and research in science teaching—to consider the problems of science in general education. In 1945, the membership was expanded and replaced the American Association for the Advancement of Science *Standing Committee on the Place of Science in Education.* The reconstituted committee known as *The Cooperative Committee for the Teaching of Science,* has been primarily interested in bringing the scientific disciplines into the program of general education at both the secondary and college levels, and in the preparation and certification of science teachers. In 1949 the objectives and interests of the new committee were reported to the AAAS Council (46).

The major objectives were given as:

1. To guide young people with promise into the ranks of effective research scientists and discerning science educators by providing opportunities appropriate to their special talents.
2. To insure the development of an understanding of the potentialities of scientific knowledge and its method in the minds of all citizens.

The committee viewed the future of American culture as dependent upon the wise use of scientific and technological developments. To say that man may predict physical events carries no implication that he may also predict the impact of these events upon our culture. The knowledge of how to use science is more important than its possession. That is to say, an understanding of the principles and methods of science and of predictable consequences of technological processes is fundamental to man's control of his environment. Man cannot control effectively that which he knows nothing about. The report implies that: 1) scientists have a particular responsibility for disclosing the alternatives to actions on matters of science in public policy; and 2) that the non-scientists need to be able to evaluate the possible choices before registering their votes.

The contributions of science to the achievement of the purposes of general education may be made in terms of a knowledge of 1) scientific principles; 2) scientific method; and 3) the social implications of science.

The committees supported the following goals for science instruction at the elementary and secondary school levels.

1. A functional understanding of the basic principles of both the biological and physical sciences.
2. An understanding of the elements of scientific methods and facility in their use.
3. Possession of scientific attitudes.

It was assumed that the needs of the non-specialist in science can be met by two years of high school science, one biological and the other a physical science, beyond the general science ordinarily required in the 7th, 8th, or 9th grades. These courses should include much biographical and historical material to show the growth of science, its philosophy, its social setting, and the social implications of science.

The committee did not attempt to construct curricula, since the research data for such work were lacking.

Summary 1940–1950

The decade from 1940 to 1950 in science teaching reflected the general education and consumer movements of the thirties and the technical manpower crisis stimulated by World War II. The result was to bring into conflict the function of science in general education and science basic to a career in specialized fields. The question of secondary school science for the scientist or science for the citizen was never clearly answered. There was a consensus, however, that all young people should have some knowledge of science as a social force and that this would demand knowing something of the nature of the scientific enterprise.

In the early part of this decade the value of science instruction, as then taught, for young people was questioned. Several attempts were made to absorb science into "core," "unified" or "integrated" science—social studies courses. The movement was greatly weakened by the events of World War II, and the resulting demand for special training in technical fields.

The consumer movement was an effort to develop a science curriculum with content that would be of some practical *use* to all youth in meeting their immediate personal-social needs. This was interpreted to mean knowledge that had immediate application in solving the problems of daily living, for example maintaining health and purchasing goods and services. The advocates of general education defined "use" in terms of intellectual tools, and an appreciation of the methods of science. All the committees agreed that science had become imperative in the education of American youth, but the concept of significant common-learnings was widely divergent.

The committees composed principally of scientists wanted more attention given to the social implications of science, supported a balanced program of physical and biological sciences, and suggested special attention be given the talented student and potential scientist. The nature of science, its methods and place in the social and economic life of the individual were seen to be of growing importance in the life of the citizen.

The committees composed mostly of educators looked upon science as a means for meeting the "needs" of individuals in various aspects of living. In this way science could be made "functional" in the lives of young people. The methods and techniques of the scientist were considered useful procedures for solving the problems of daily living. The "scientific attitudes" were recognized as worthy goals for all students in science courses and at all levels.

Every committee supported, in some degree, the importance of science in the maintenance of a "free society" and democratic ideals. These ends would be accomplished through developing a citizenry informed in science and by maintaining an adequate supply of scientific and technical manpower. The curriculum and teaching procedures necessary to achieve these goals were not clearly defined.

Most of the committees failed to mention modern learning theory and its relation to science teaching. The philosophical assumptions underlying the concepts of "general education" were often hazy or contradictory. The result was that curriculum reforms in science and improved teaching procedures did not materialize in the schools. The seeds were sown, however, for curriculum developments that were to emerge in the next decade.

While the status of science in the secondary school curriculum was never weaker than at the start of this period (1940), the stimulus of the "atomic age" and the acceleration of scientific and technical development following World War II reaffirmed the need for education in the sciences. In brief, the 1940–1950 period represented a decade of divergent points of view about science teaching. Each committee did agree, however, that the science curriculum of the past was not suitable for the youth then in school.

All the committees that considered the science offerings in schools recommended a continuous program of science instruction from kindergarten through high school. They were not unaware of the problems involved in their recommendation—the shortage of qualified teachers, the lack of facilities and equipment and the need to study the grade placement of different science concepts.

The general biology course continued to gain in enrollment throughout the 1940–1950 decade. Nearly all the high schools in America were offering the course and in 1950, 21.7% of all high school students were enrolled in a biology class. The special biological subjects—physiology, botany, zoology—had a combined enrollment of 1.2% of the students in high school. Several of the curriculum committees during this period noted the growing enrollment in biology and pointed out that it was the biology teachers who must now assume the responsibility of conveying to the majority of youth most of what they will learn about the nature of science.

VIII

The Crisis in Science Education and a Reappraisal, 1950–1960

THE DECADE from 1950 to 1960 has been described as one of "confusion and crisis" in science education. Dozens of state and national committees have published statements about needed improvements in secondary school science teaching. Articles expressing the opinions of individuals run into the thousands. The Second Session of the Eighty-Fifth Congress of the United States recorded 1600 pages of testimony in twenty-two days on the question of "science and education for national defense."

Professional societies of scientists and technologists have reactivated their education committees and proposed policies for science teaching. Industries, either individually or through their Foundations, have developed new teaching aids, stimulated curriculum studies and supported programs of teacher education in science.

The National Science Foundation has taken the leadership in stimulating and supporting the development of new curricula and teaching resources in the sciences and mathematics. Hundreds of institutes have been organized to assist in realizing the potentialities of new curricula through a retraining of teachers.

The problems leading to a concern about secondary school science teaching following 1950 had been developing for some time. Perhaps the basic factor was the accelerated growth of science and technology following the close of World War II. The vast amount of scientific knowledge that had been accumulating in the last hundred years, the "break-throughs" in science and technology symbolized by biotics, electron microscopes, atomic fusion and space probes, all caused speculations about the nature of education in the sciences.

The application of scientific and technical knowledge to the production of goods and the thirst of industry for more knowledge to nourish industrialization have led to a continuously narrowing gap between research and its application to industrial techniques and products. It is these products of technology that impress the average man; they have given him the comforts and conveniences characterized by modern living. The relationship between science and technology, especially the part that science plays, is still vague in the minds of most people. To many scientists this is the fault of the way science is taught to young people.

Between 1950–1960 it became apparent that few of the major economic, political or social problems of our society or of modern civilization could be discussed to their fullest import in the absence of a scientist. An understanding of science was becoming imperative in the education of all people. The nature of this education had not yet evolved.

The vast increase in the volume of organized knowledge, with its growing complexity and its inaccessibility to the nonspecialists, has posed a serious problem to the curriculum maker for some time now. How to keep high school courses at the point where recent scientific achievements will find a way into the intellectual life of everyone has been an unsolved problem. Then there is the task of getting rid of the inert knowledge in courses to make room for the more significant and newer concepts.

The biological fields since mid-century have taken on new vigor. New research tools and techniques have advanced discoveries faster than anticipated. The unifying concepts in genetics along with the research on DNA, have provided a foundation for a science of "biology." Researchers in the special fields now have a basis for communication in the theoretical aspects of DNA. There are other examples. These achievements suggest the need to reformulate the biology courses intended for general education.

Several problems in secondary school education were conspicuous between 1950–1960. At the start of this century only 8.4% of the youth in America between 14–17 years of age were in high school; by 1960 the number had increased to 70% and the trend was upward. The range of abilities and interests reflected in a 60% sample of an age range that included 8.5 million young people is overwhelming. Furthermore, these pupils were distributed among 22,000 high schools of which more than 14,000 had a graduating class of less than 100. Curriculum planning and course development had not been able to keep pace with the kinds of problems presented by this situation.

The demand for higher education by a larger fraction of the high school graduates brought new pressures on the high schools during the fifties. Many critics felt that the high schools had been growing lax in offering the type of courses that "would better prepare for the intellectual life of the college." The primary concern was that the gifted and the talented student was not being challenged to his capacity.

While some critics focused their attention on the science curriculum others felt that the greatest need was in the improvement of teaching and that this would come about if teachers were better trained. Throughout the decade beginning with 1950 the number of college graduates with science majors who desired to teach dropped each year, while enrollments in science increased. At no time during the 1950–1960 period was it possible to fill but a fraction of the teaching vacancies in science with qualified teachers.

In many sections of the country the needs for school construction, science facilities and equipment were not adequately met. Trained curriculum workers and supervisors in science were in small supply. The National Defense Education Act passed in 1958 was an effort to relieve some of these difficulties.

Only minor attention had been given to theories and research in human learning in the past fifteen years. The characteristics of the time indicated the need for a greater efficiency in learning and better teaching techniques. But there was not adequate psychological research available to develop the necessary educational hypotheses.

These conditions in science and in education were not entirely unrecognized. The Harvard Committee (73) and the Steelman Report (79) published after the close of World War II, recognized that the time had arrived for a curriculum reorientation in the sciences. A number of educators and scientists as individuals also sought to be heard. The events, however, that resulted in the "space age" were sufficient to activate those interested in science teaching to a massive effort of curriculum redevelopment. To fully appreciate the significance of the work to improve science education in American schools during the 1950–1960 period the problem needs to be viewed in a perspective that includes the social, economic, scientific, political and educational developments that were characteristic of the period.

The first major effort to review the teaching of biology in American secondary schools during the 1950–1960 decade was carried out at the *Southeastern Conference on Biology Teaching,* held during the summer of 1954 (15). Eighty-five high school and college teachers met for a period of ten days to discuss the problems of biology teaching. Represented at the conference were high school biology teachers, college biology teachers, science education specialists; administrators from colleges, public schools, and state departments of education.

The major objectives of the conference were: 1) to establish the proper role and the major contributions of the various biological sciences to teacher training; 2) to identify some of the major problems found in the teaching of high school and college biology; 3) to develop suggestions and recommendations for the improvement of biology teaching in high school; 4) to develop plans for the implementation of the recommendations of the conference.

Six biological scientists prepared written summary statements on how their special fields could and should contribute to the training of biology teachers. From these papers much of the resource material for the development of high school curriculum and the teacher training programs was formulated.

Sixty problems concerning the teaching of biology were identified, of which twenty were chosen for detailed discussion. Only those parts of the report related to curriculum will be reviewed here.

The committee first reviewed and discussed papers in the following biological fields: 1) heredity and development; 2) evolution and paleontology; 3) morphology; 4) taxonomy; 5) physiology and health; and 6) ecology and conservation. From these presentations a series of basic principles for curriculum development were established. The committee pointed out the importance of the biology "specialist" becoming a "generalist" when it comes to developing curriculum materials for high school courses.

The major problems of biology teaching identified at the conference were: 1) availability of teachers with adequate training in biology; the group was aware, however, that 59% of the high school biology teachers at that time (1952) had a college major in biological sciences; 2) relationship of biology to the rest of the high school program; 3) adequacy of coverage in important content areas of biology; 4) adequacy of text and other teaching materials; 5) adequacy of laboratory equipment and outdoor study areas; 6) effectiveness of biology programs in meeting the needs and interests of students; 7) effectiveness of testing and evaluation procedures; and 8) extent of assistance, leadership, and supervision by administrators.

The conference representatives were of the opinion that biology courses should be designed to meet the needs and interests of individual students. Course objectives should be both general and local in character embracing the principles of biology with local applications. The following goals for teaching secondary school biology were suggested: 1) an understanding of the basic principles of biology; 2) an understanding of themselves (man) and of human life; 3) an understanding of how the organism and physical environment in a given situation form a community with many complex interrelationships; 4) an understanding of how biology can be used in later life; 5) an understanding of scientific methods and attitudes through experiences in the biology course; 6) a positive approach to physical and mental health; 7) avocational interests and appreciations related to living things.

To achieve these goals demands student participation in a wide range of learning activities and the use of appropriate correlative teaching techniques. The high school teacher should exert the leadership for developing needed textual and instructional materials. Special opportunities for talented students and for those with individual interests were recommended.

It was emphatically stated that field work and laboratory experience with living materials should be used as a means for developing in high school students some understanding of the methods, approaches and attitudes of biological scientists. The group also recommended that the work in biology should be integrated into the total program of the secondary school wherever the opportunity exists.

The *North Central Conference on Biology Teaching* was held in 1955 at Cheboygan, Michigan (9). A total of 87 high school science teachers, college biology teachers, science education specialists and public school administrators met to study: 1) "the contributions of biology to living and to develop a set of basic principles and practical experiences which are essential for biology teachers and pupils"; 2) to analyze some of the most important problems of biology teaching at various levels of instruction; 3) "to develop a set of recommendations for the solution of the selected problems"; and 4) "to formulate plans by state teams for implementing the recommendations." The work of this committee was patterned similarly to that of the *Southeastern Conference on Biology Teaching*, held in 1954. Research biologists in various fields were invited to prepare papers as background material on what they considered to be significant subject matter for the high school teacher, and then to suggest the experiences and methods by which these materials might be presented to students.

The conferees recognized that local conditions must influence what can be done in the study of biology. After deliberations some of the recommendations were: 1) there should be a year of biology, preferably in the tenth grade; 2) the course should be designed for all students but must provide for individual differences; 3) special opportunities should be provided for capable students, and for those who plan to become biologists. Furthermore, the high school program should be directed toward understanding the methods, approaches and attitudes of science and how these differ from the non-sciences.

It was recommended that the curriculum in biology be re-examined, particularly in terms of topics that could be taught at grade levels before high school. There was a consensus that 1) current scientific developments and social trends should influence the content of biology courses; 2) course adjustments are needed to meet the problem of urbanization; and 3) the whole biology course needs to be up-graded in intellectual content.

In the teaching of biology the success of the methods used was thought to be dependent upon the teacher and the total environment as well as upon the learner. The textbook should be used as a source of information and as a tool but not as a set course of study. Definite attempts should be made to take advantage of a wider variety of community and natural resources. It was felt that more use could be made of museums, zoos, botanical gardens, vacant lots, and the landscaping within cities.

The administrative set-up of a school has much to do with effective biology teaching and recommendations were made to help teachers obtain: 1) an increase in academic freedom; 2) a decrease in class interruption; and 3) a better program of in-service education. The high school biology teachers expressed a desire to know what other biology teachers were doing, and recommendations were made for increasing communications with other members of the profession.

In 1954 the Division of Biology and Agriculture, National Academy of Sciences–National Research Council, established a *Committee on Educational Policies* to consider problems of biological education. At a later time, as an outcome of these earlier discussions, sub-committees were set up to explore the problems of biology teaching from the elementary school through collegiate and adult education. Other subcommittees were appointed to consider special problems such as laboratory work, textbooks, guidance materials, films, and teacher education. Only the committee reports that have relevance to high school biology will be summarized here.

The program of the Committee on Educational Policies grew out of a *Conference on Biological Education*, held in Washington, D.C., March 10, 1953 (25), and sponsored by the National Academy of Sciences–National Research Council, the following question was discussed in detail: "How can the educational system in biology adjust itself most properly to the change of emphasis taking place in the biological sciences away from preoccupation with specific living forms into the direction of principles and mechanisms of life processes?"

It was felt that major changes were needed in biological education at all levels and for both general and professional education. The following resolution was issued: "In view of the rapid development of the biological sciences, it is desirable that educational and instructional objectives and practices be subject to continuous and concerted study. Be it therefore resolved that a policy committee be established within the structure of the Division of Biology and Agriculture of the National Research Council, to confer with and advise those individuals and organizations that are most intimately concerned with biological education in its many facets as to the present and prospective demands upon, and needs of, the biological sciences."

After reviewing a number of reports on biological education the *Committee on Educational Policies* of the NAS–NRC concluded (1) that any discussions on biological education should consider "the accelerating growth and diversification of the biological sciences; the need for continuing reappraisal of fundamental concepts; the increasing demand for specialists, but specialists with broad knowledge and outlook; the expanding significance of the sciences in human affairs; and the concomitant need for public understanding and support of scientific inquiry."

The committee was in general accord on the following points:

1. "There is need for agreement among the educators and scientists in this country as to what constitutes biology to be taught in the high school, college, and graduate levels."

2. "Biology as taught at the high school level in many areas, does not arouse much interest in the student. There is need for improving the training and qualifications of high school biology teachers, and correspondingly, there is need for stimulating people to go into the teaching of biology."

3. "There is need for a 'core curriculum' in biology for the student who plans to become a biologist as compared with biology courses given the student who does not intend to continue in this field."

4. "There is need for wider exchange of ideas among biology teachers at all levels, through the media of journals, professional organizations, national societies, etc."

5. "In conclusion, there is need for a committee composed of biologists, educators, textbook publishers, science writers, and representatives of industry to cover the whole spectrum of biological education from the high school level up."

The values to be derived from a study of biology were stated as follows: "The committee believes that a basic knowledge of biology should be a part of everybody's education . . . The high school course should be designed to give students an appreciation of biology as an open and growing field, full of unresolved problems, and full of profound implications for man's life. It should give the student experience in the scientific approach to problems and confidence in science as a major instrumentality of man's exploring intellect. It should give students an abiding interest in organisms, including themselves, and make them aware of the significance of biological occupations and avocations."

The extensive vocabulary found in biology courses caused much concern. "One of the shortcomings of textbooks and courses is often that the student may become so impressed with need for learning a new vocabulary as to lose sight of larger objectives. Moreover, much confusion has arisen in the use of terms and units in biology simply because of the way biology has grown. Many labels may be applied to different forms of what later turns out to be a single type of entity; conversely, terms may change meanings as discovery proceeds, but people may use the terms in all senses from the earliest to the latest. Much of this is inevitable in an actively growing realm of inquiry, but some difficulties can be avoided by helping students develop an increasingly critical faculty, a steadily deepening appreciation of the relationships and contrasts between fact and theory, phenomena and concept, reality and label. Authors and teachers, meanwhile, have a special problem and a special responsibility in regard to terminology."

The sub-section on the *Improvement of Textbooks* of the *Committee on Educational Policies* surveyed the shortcomings of the modern textbook in biology (23). It recognized textbooks as a basic requisite of biological education but felt, however, that they tend to be conservative, to lag behind the development of a discipline, and that all too frequently efforts at modernizing involve little more than sprinkling a sauce of late news flashes over an essentially archaic presentation. "Whether accurate and contemporary in outlook or not, many textbooks are written with an overwhelming finality which misleads the student into believing that he has mastered the full scope of the subject as soon as he has covered the book. Few textbooks succeed in portraying their science as living, developing human behavior; few, despite a first chapter genuflection toward 'scientific method', attempt to give the student a clear understanding of how we have arrived at our present state of knowledge—and ignorance."

In the development of new textbooks or in the reordering of courses, it was suggested that a "committee of top-flight experts representative of the varied facets of the discipline be asked to lay out rather fully what is presently known, what can be said of the relative significance of specific data and principles, what the emergent trends and possible future directions of the area may be." There was a consensus that "by this way more first-rank research scientists can be brought into the textbook-preparing process, whether they themselves carry the task through to a published book or not."

A further recommendation was that a board of review for textbooks should be initiated "to make comprehensive and critical reviews widely available." It was felt that school administrators, lay boards and many teachers were not in a position to make critical judgments as to the content of textbooks. It would not be a function of the board to impose any pattern of conformity or style. "The proposed board would not only review books after publication but would make its services available to publishers upon request for prepublication review of manuscripts." This plan was later rejected in favor of the preparation of a statement on criteria for the preparation of textbooks.

The *Subcommittee on Instructional Materials and Publications* of the National Academy of Sciences–National Research Council, after reviewing the problem of textbooks in biological education, prepared a report on *Criteria for Preparation and Selection of Science Textbooks* (11). Little had been written up to this time (1957) on the selection of textbooks in biology, particularly with any rationale in mind. The major criteria for the preparation and selection of science textbooks as they were developed by the committee follow:

Point of View

Some statistical evidence and much general observation lead to the conclusion that high school and college courses in science do not yield a higher percentage of students with scientific attitudes toward problems than do nonscience courses. If this is indeed true, the cause must be sought in teaching, unless one is willing to believe that students of high school and college age have already become so inflexible as to be unable to acquire characteristics usually described as scientific attitudes—healthy skepticism, open-mindedness, willingness to apply new data to problems considered settled. It is conceivable that some students at this stage may have lost their malleability. Science teaching, however, must be predicated on the assumption that most have not.

Upon looking back on their own schooling, most scientists can remember instructors and textbooks who failed to exemplify scientific attitudes. Science teaching and science textbooks, especially at elementary levels, are too often authoritarian—the very antithesis of scientific attitudes and modes of thought. Many books present theory and fact as though there were no difference between them and as though both were settled for all time. In contrast, the best books and the best teaching show clearly that science is a search for knowledge and that mankind is very far from the end of the search in any branch of science; they inspire both a love of learning and a zeal for the quest.

We believe that *authoritarian teaching* of science as found in many textbooks does much to close minds, not open them; to make robots, not thinkers; to discourage, not encourage further work in science; to inhibit, not promote attempts to apply scientific methods to the numerous problems one meets daily in every walk of life.

In many courses and textbooks, subjects are presented as though the course or textbook contained all the available facts and theory on the subject at hand, when, in fact, no book or course can present more than a *selection* of fact and theory. Capable students are unlikely to choose a field for a career if it is shown to them as an apparently closed and completed story.

We believe, therefore, that all science textbooks should exhibit the following basic characteristics:

1) They should show the difference between fact and theory, between the solid core of verified knowledge and on-going intellectual exploration, between reaffirmed theory and the continuing re-evaluation of interpretations. If students are frequently reminded that what they are reading is the *present state of knowledge* or *the present interpretation of observations and experimental results,* they will be more likely to think of science as a *process,* as well as a more or less organized body of observations and explanatory theories. Truth in science is continuously being sought and is continuously changing as new observations are made and new theories are evolved to explain them. *The aim of science teaching is to show the nature of science as well as the science of an aspect of nature.*

2) They should make it very clear that the course is a *selection*

of presently-known fact and more or less accepted theory. Occasional or frequent reminders that portions (sentences to chapters) could be expanded into whole books or shelves of books can help to increase the reader's appreciation of the scope of the subject presented.

3) They should *cite unsolved problems*. Frequently the development of a topic offers golden opportunities for showing gaps in current information or theory. Appreciation of the need for research can be fostered by discussing problems now under investigation or in need of investigation.

4) They should show the *relationships* of the given subject to other fields of science and to broad problems of humanity. Student interest can be quickened by the occasional, if not frequent, consideration of what a fact or theory is *good for*. How often are students shown the range of impact of scientific fact and theory on intellectual history and human affairs?

Criteria for the Content of Textbooks

1) *Adequacy of coverage*. Books are often criticized for inadequacy of material by those who have not judged the product in relation to the purpose for which the book was written. Furthermore, users too often seem to want—with consequent pressure on authors and publishers—a storehouse of factual information rather than a well-ordered synthesis of basic concepts and principles. No text today can be complete; and even if a 'complete' book were possible, it would be undesirable because it would tend to preclude other reading representing different viewpoints and interpretations. It follows, therefore, that a teacher who discards a good book for a poor one on the basis of the omission of some relatively unimportant topic (often one the user could best supply) does his students an injustice.

2) *Up-to-dateness*. The science text selected should represent the most modern thinking available, articulated with the cumulative store of relevant concepts from the past. This criterion is often distorted by merely superimposing a seductive façade of recent research results and references upon a fundamental framework that should have long since gone into the discard. Successive editions of a text should particularly be scrutinized to determine whether the framework or only the façade has been 'brought up to date.'

3) *Point of view.* Does the book present, as advocated above, scientific methodology, the scientific process (and throughout, not merely in a lip-service chapter)? And does it open some of the vast vistas of unanswered questions that make up the challenge of the future?

4) *Suitability for students.* Too often the teacher selecting a text judges in terms of its impression on him, without sufficiently considering its suitability for students at the level of development represented in his course. Authors, too, have been known to write books more for colleagues than for students. The selector should ask himself such questions as the following. Does the book require background his students have not yet acquired through courses or from general experience or concurrent reading? Is the amount of terminology within the student's grasp? Are new terms properly defined and intelligently used? (Fortunately, biology seems gradually to be discarding the idea that even elementary courses must be terminology memory-mills.) It has long been known that if terms are to be remembered and available, they must be meaningful, must be useful, and must be used. At the same time, we certainly do not mean that there should be no 'stretching' of the student, even the average student, with new words or mature language. If at each grade level we assumed that the student could not handle languages he had not been exposed to before, when would the student advance beyond the primers?

5) *Logical coherence.* A textbook should build from simple to complex in proper steps; topics should be developed in a logical sequence, not as an assemblage of facts arranged by categories. Rarely if ever is there only one 'right' outline, but the author should be able to show a reasoned basis for the organization he has adopted, and the user should be able to see the organizational plan without excessive effort or persuasion. The requirement of a logical sequence does not preclude repetition of the same material in different contexts; a discipline may have more than one dimension. On the other hand, a text fails to achieve its proper function if it is so loosely structured as to be amenable to random recombination of its parts.

6) *Accuracy.* Author and publisher should have done everything possible to insure accuracy. Carping criticism of minor obvious errors would seem unjustified, but many small slips

should alert the selector to the possibility of more basic faults. Most serious are uncritical acceptance of interpretations, dogmatism, and errors in important factual content.

7) *Summaries.* For some types of textbooks, end-of-chapter summaries can be valuable teaching aids. An alternative method is to use marginal notes summarizing each section or paragraph and so phrased as to form a chapter summary when read consecutively. In no case should summaries offer an escape from reading the chapter, but they can usefully highlight the main points. Summaries at the ends of chapters can also be used to develop transitions between chapters or to point up unsolved problems and questions.

8) *Study questions.* These are not necessarily essential but can be valuable if they do not merely trigger regurgitation. The temptation to use rote questions will be less if the development of the subject is more than merely factual. Questions should be graded in difficulty and should offer students real challenges by requiring a search for answers outside the textbook, by posing problems not adumbrated in the text, and by inclusion of optional questions for students with the inclination and aptitude to penetrate the subject more deeply.

9) *Bibliographies.* In elementary texts extensive reference lists, particularly to material far beyond the comprehension of the student, are relatively useless. Furthermore, if the book is to find general use, the references must be readily accessible sources. In more advanced texts more comprehensive reference lists can be very valuable, but there, too, all citations should be scrutinized for pertinence. A reference list is more helpful if it includes 'capsule' annotations, especially to show what part of a reference is pertinent and what light it throws on some topic in the chapter.

10) *Indexes.* Textbook indexes are frequently so incomplete or so poorly designed as to be doubtfully worth the extra pages. The main purpose of an index is to enable a reader to find topics, and especially major discussions of topics, under words the reader is likely to look for. A good index is comprehensive and is built around ideas and concepts as well as around names of things. Identifying major discussions by such devices as boldface page citations increases the index's usefulness.

Criteria for the Form of Textbooks

1) *Clarity and readability*. No matter how good the material, it might as well remain locked in the author's mind if he fails to transmit it with crystal clarity. If to clarify the author can add fluency, verve, apt analogy, even a sprinkling of humor, the student will not only read with pleasure but will grasp and retain more of what he reads. Texts with these qualities are rare in the second-hand market, since even a textbook with these attributes often becomes a permanent addition to the student's library. But style is not all. There have also been texts that read like novels but lacked real substance and lost their appeal upon more mature reflection.

2) *Illustrations*. Illustrations can be invaluable teaching aids, merely decorative, or both. Ideally they should be both instructive and pictorially effective. If merely decorative, their worth is highly dubious. To be instructive they should be so completely integrated with the text that the text is relatively unintelligible without them and the illustrations relatively meaningless without the accompanying exposition. This implies that illustrations should be as near the appropriate textual material as possible. We also deplore the long-standing practice of uncritically borrowing illustrations from other sources, irrespective of their accuracy or appropriateness. Poor composition and reproduction can similarly vitiate the effectiveness of illustrations. Authors are often tempted to include so much in a single figure as to confuse or discourage the reader. Photographs, particularly photomicrographs, lose much of their effect if reproduction is of less than superior quality.

3) *Aids to emphasis*. Judicious use of headings, boldface, and italics can assist the student by highlighting conceptual relations and important definitions and terms. But when overdone, the effectiveness of such devices diminishes rapidly.

4) *Format*. Attractive typography and binding can help make the use of a book a pleasurable experience, but a selection based primarily on these elements is certainly unwise.

Suggested Procedures for Selecting a Text

Using these criteria, how does the conscientious teacher set about selecting a suitable text for a given course? Obviously, the thoroughness of his search and the time required will depend on the number of books available and his familiarity with the older ones, and on his own involvement in the subject. If the field is his major interest, selection will be simplified, and he may skip some of the steps listed. If it isn't, and he has the interests of students fully in mind, he will do well to exercise the utmost care.

1) Scanning the available books may be adequate for a rough screening, but those under serious consideration should be read.

2) The selector should watch for *critical* reviews which, presumably, are written by experts. However, he himself should apply as much critical judgment as possible to the reviews, for they may be biased or wrong.

3) If the book includes any substantial amount of relatively unfamiliar material, expert critical advice should be sought.

4) It may be desirable, especially at introductory levels, to try selected chapters on students who seem to possess critical capacities but have not progressed so far as to be unable to judge comprehensibility and readablility for those who will be using the text.

5) Before he makes his choice, the selector should carefully compare the available books, matching them point by point against a set of such definite and explicit criteria as those herein outlined.

The earlier meetings of the *Subcommittee on Pre-College Education* (57) were devoted to a study of those phases of biology instruction in secondary schools which appeared crucial. The following statements were developed to represent problems and issues in high school biology teaching but should not be interpreted as recommendations:

1. *Laboratory.* "For indoor laboratory work we need manuals at different academic levels containing really good, fresh instructive experiments. For outdoor laboratories more effort needs to be devoted to the development of school camping, school gardens and forests, and school projects in study and improvement of the children's own communities."

2. *Advanced Biology Courses.* Most secondary schools have

only a tenth grade general biology course. There is a place for junior and senior courses built upon this introduction—courses in natural history, botany, and zoology, in technician fields, and in the so-called earth sciences.

3. *Course interrelations.* Attention needs to be given to relating instruction by teachers in the different subjects, that is, biology apparatus might be constructed in shop, writing biology themes in English and discussions on the impact of science in social studies classes.

4. *Communication skills.* There is abundant evidence of student deficiencies in the ability to speak and write effectively. One possible cause is the lack of opportunity to practice these skills. A journal in which high school students could publish science articles to be read by other students might provide a stimulus.

5. *Library and laboratory facilities.* It was suggested that mobile reference libraries and laboratory equipment in schools be developed where there are not sufficient resources in each classroom.

6. *The superior student.* A plan to provide college credit for superior work in high school was seen as a "spur to the improvement of high school teaching."

The committee felt that more support should be given to the use of outdoor "laboratories" in instruction, but was not enthusiastic in their support of advanced biology courses in high school.

The Committee on Educational Policies of the National Academy of Sciences—National Research Council in 1954 established a *Subcommittee on Instructional Materials and Publications* (58). One of the first concerns of this committee was to consider the problem of laboratory instruction and field work in biology.

In the earlier meetings of the committee the following points of view were established as working guides:

Biologists in all fields concur in the conviction that opportunities for students to conduct observations and experiments on biological phenomena and organisms through field studies and properly planned laboratory work are an indispensable part of most biology courses; laboratory work is especially important in basic courses in secondary schools and colleges. These are crucial courses having a two-fold importance: 1) They are the main avenue through which our future citizenry will become acquainted with the problems, methods, accomplishments, and values of the biological sciences; 2) Through them students may be so challenged by the opportunities, the unsolved questions, the human significance of biology as to embark upon professional carreers in the life sciences and their applied offshoots.

The committee noted "in a distressingly large number of high schools and even in some colleges, the pressures of mounting enrollments and inadequate facilities, the ineptitude and lack of enthusiasm of some teachers, the notion that students learn as well from demonstrations and films as from laboratory work they do themselves, have led to drastic reduction or even total abandonment of laboratory and field study. Elsewhere, though 'laboratory' remains on schedule, what is offered is so pedestrian and unimaginative, so unlikely to challenge the student's powers as to be almost worse than no laboratory work at all."

To meet the educational problems of effective laboratory work, the pressures of increasing class enrollments, and the encroachments upon the time the teacher has for planning, and the problem of the diversity of subjects in high school biology, the committee decided "to pool the talents of the best teachers by publishing source books of dynamic and challenging, tested and practical laboratory and field projects for students of different levels and in different special subjects." A working plan was developed for involving imaginative high school biology teachers and university biologists from a wide array of biological disciplines to prepare a source book of laboratory and field studies for high school biology.

The *Sourcebook of Laboratory and Field Studies in Biology* was prepared during a writing conference held at Michigan State University for two months during the summer of 1957 (47). The writing team was composed of twenty high school biology teachers and ten biologists from colleges and universities.

Initial steps in preparing for the *Sourcebook* were to make some decisions about the purposes of high school general biology and how it might be taught. The *Panel on High School Biology* courses, therefore, "sought to define the broad goals of laboratory and field studies and the philosophy which should underlie the whole program." The next step was to examine "the content of modern biology in search of basic dimensions which should appear in the book and in courses . . ." It was recognized that "no single organization fits all courses," therefore the *Sourcebook* was designed to be useful to every teacher regardless of his course plan.

The objectives accepted for the teaching of high school biology were:

1. A major function "of laboratory and field studies is to show students that biology is a living science full of interesting and intriguing questions, not just a series of 'cut and draw' school experiences."

2. "Some exercises must be concerned with observation, dissection and the transmission of basic factual material, but many are designed (a) to present problems to the students; (b) to permit the collection of relevant data; and (c) to lead students to relate the data to their own knowledge so that they can formulate hypotheses which they can test. Wherever possible, learning in biology should involve an active quest by students that makes them, for the moment at least, scientists in search of discovery."

3. "Laboratory and field studies should also lead students to understand biology in its present stage of development as a science. Various aspects of the teaching of biology represent historical periods in its development and in some high school courses the teaching is unfortunately still confined to the earliest of these stages. The following phases can be identified in the development of biology: (a) the taxonomic, in which the emphasis is on recognizing and classifying the individuals with which the science is concerned; (b) the static descriptive, in which these objects are described in static or morphological terms; (c) the dynamic or analytical, in which theories of chemistry and physics are applied to explain biological proc-

esses; and (d) the organismic or holistic, the most recent, in which explanatory concepts develop from within biology itself but include theories from the physical sciences, and in which the main effort is to put together all information on the objects of study so as to evolve an integrated organismic or ecological picture. If students are to understand biology as a science, they should have experience with all of these phases. Moreover, they should have opportunities to appreciate that biology equally emphasizes the individual experience or event and the regularities called laws. They should be helped at every stage to see biology as an open and growing field in which a great many problems still remain unsolved."

4. "Furthermore, the biology laboratory experience should be the kind that will lead some students to the discovery of rewarding avocations and others to an exciting life work."

5. "Finally, the course in biology should develop in students confidence in science as a dependable aid to the solution of many human problems. To accomplish this, biology as well as other sciences must be presented to students as a serviceable and dependable intellectual tool that can be used, despite certain limitations, not only to satisfy the aesthetic needs of a few specialists, but to solve many of the world's practical problems, and to gain for humanity as a whole an intellectual understanding of the nature of things not achievable without it."

The dimensions of a high school biology course were described as follows:

1. "Because minute follows minute, page follows page, and exercise follows exercise, courses, textbooks and instructional aids like the *Sourcebook* stand in constant danger of representing multidimensional realms of knowledge and inquiry as unidimensional systems. A realization of the multidimensional character of any science, scholarly discipline, or practical field can nevertheless evolve within the individual intellect. This is precisely what we as teachers want to help our students achieve. We believe, therefore, that attempts to define the major parameters of biology serve a useful purpose. Doing so will help to keep before us two things important for

teaching: a) many pathways through the system, biology, are possible and will achieve the objectives of a general course, provided a number of the major parameters are represented, and b) we should always help the students to see how the specific topic, the individual exercise, relates to the whole panorama which should eventually rise to view in the student's mind."

2. "It must be emphasized that *no* conceptual scheme can or should be proposed as *the* best scheme. Any number of schemes can be conceived. In the high school course, however, we should emphasize the nature of scientific inquiry, and should focus primary attention on principles. At the same time, we should acquaint students with the diversity of individuals that comprise the living world."

3. "There are at least three dimensions in a study of biology. The three we use reflect the three objectives set for the high school course: a) the processes of scientific investigation; b) the variety of organisms; and c) approaches, concepts and principles as developed in the outline. Others could replace them or be added to them, including levels of biological organization, dynamic relationships among these levels, types of approach, tools of investigation, disciplines, etc."

The committee recognized that there are many course organizations possible. The starting point may be any organism and any aspect of biology, and the course may proceed in varied directions. But whatever the organization, the course should sample the major areas of inquiry and the biologies of particular kinds of organisms; it should be so planned as to lead finally to the development of a coherent view of biology; and it should be presented in such a way as to exemplify the nature of science.

The material developed for the secondary school biology laboratory and field work was organized to fit the following course outline.

1. ORGANISMS LIVING IN THEIR PARTICULAR ENVIRONMENTS ARE THE PRIMARY SUBJECTS OF BIOLOGY
   a. Introductory Survey of Natural Communities
   b. Introductory Field Survey of One Group of Organisms

c. Laboratory Communities
d. Study of a Single Species

2. THE DIVERSITY OF ORGANISMS
   a. Understanding the Concepts of Biological Classification
   b. Major Phyla and Classes of Organisms
   c. Use of Classification Manuals

3. SOME ESSENTIAL CHEMISTRY
   a. The Nature of Matter
   b. Properties of Solutions, Colloidal Systems and Suspensions
   c. Chemical Reactions; Energetics; Catalysis
   d. Constitution of Cells

4. THE ORGANISM AS A DYNAMIC OPEN SYSTEM: INTRODUCTION TO THE BASIC ORGANISMIC FUNCTIONS
   a. Obtaining Matter and Energy
   b. Using Matter and Energy for Life Processes
   c. Release of Byproduct Matter and Energy
   d. Reacting to the Changing Environment (Irritability and Response)

5. MAINTENANCE OF THE INDIVIDUAL
   a. Nutrients and Modes of Obtaining Them
   b. The Internal Environment and Internal Transport (Circulatory Mechanisms)
   c. Metabolism
   d. Gas Exchange
   e. Supportive Structures
   f. Movement
   g. Coordination and Integration

6. MAINTENANCE OF THE SPECIES
   a. Reproduction
   b. Heredity
   c. Development

7. THE ORGANISM IN ITS ECOLOGICAL SETTING
   a. Relationships of the Individual to its Environment
   b. Relationships Among Individuals of the Same Species Forming a Single Population
   c. Relationships Among Individuals of Different Species Within an Ecological Community
   d. Human Ecology

    e. The Hierarchy of Group and Environmental Relationships:
      Organisms, Aggregations, Societies, Communities of Differ-
      ent Levels of Size and Complexity, World Biota

8. EVOLUTION OF ORGANISMS AND THEIR ENVIRON-
   MENTS
    a. Time Scales: Measurement and Duration
    b. Theories of Origin and Early History of Earth
    c. Theories of Origin of Organisms in Relation to Environment
    d. The Facts of Evolution: Examples from the Record
    e. How Evolution Has Come About: Theories on the Mecha-
      nisms of Evolution

The committee recognized that:

1. "Learning to report observations, experimental findings and
   interpretations is an important phase of laboratory and field
   work."

2. "Laboratory and field studies, of course, comprise but part
   of the biology program. That program as a whole must form
   an integrated experience for the student. Laboratory and
   field studies must therefore be continuously planned and developed in relation to reading, discussion, consultation with
   resource persons and evaluative procedures."

The preliminary edition of the *Sourcebook* was tried out by
a number of secondary school biology teachers and revised. The
final edition was published commercially in 1960 (48), (49).

In 1956, the Committee on Educational Policies, National
Academy of Sciences–National Research Council, sponsored a
booklet on *Career Opportunities in Biology* (80). The publication was "in response to repeated requests for information and
guidance received from biologists and biological societies."
Questions about the nature of the biological sciences, career
opportunities and their educational requirements were explored.

In 1958, the Committee on Educational Policies, Division of
Biology and Agriculture, National Academy of Sciences–National Research Council, in an unofficial staff paper, summa-

rized many of the current ideas about the teaching of biology (24).

In the report the purposes which underly biological education were given as follows:

1. "For students in general, as future citizens, instruction in the sciences should transmit, first, an understanding and appreciation of science as an activity of the human mind, an ongoing, unending search for knowledge; second, a substantial grasp of the nature of things as thus far revealed by scientific work, with the hope that the citizen will continue to modify and supplement this learning througout his life; third, an understanding of the role of science and its offspring, technology, in every human culture, every stage of history, but especially in our times and the future in which students will live. Whether the student eventually works in agriculture, industry, government, business, commerce, education, arts or sciences, he is likely to need some part of a changing body of scientific knowledge in his own work."

2. "This basic science must include understanding, knowledge and appreciation of biology. Biological knowledge is important both for the intellectual insights it affords and its enormous practical consequences through agriculture, medicine, anthropology and psychology for the life of mankind."

3. "In view of its high aims and unquestionable importance, science instruction must obviously be as good as we can make it. That it generally falls short of what it can be is a conclusion of most observers and analysts who have recently examined science teaching." Some of the suggestions for improving this undesirable situation were:

   a. "better schools (broad and informed public support, sound administration, good buildings, including laboratories and libraries, adequate equipment and supplies, proper teacher-pupil ratios, more money for education, etc.);

   b. "better teachers (salary scales and policies competitive with other professions, better preparatory and continuing education, sound certification policy, helpful rather than restrictive supervision, etc.);

   c. "better instructional programs (courses and curricula in

pace with growing knowledge and social change, emphasis on basic principles and understanding to which knowledge can be added throughout life, proper emphasis on laboratory and individualized effort, provision for especially able, average and slow students, etc.)"

4. "Biologists and other scientists can help advance us along all three paths but, because of their special knowledge, they have special responsibility to help improve content of instructional programs and competence of teachers."

5. "Some shortcomings of contemporary science teaching are attributable to the gap between scholars in the forefront of investigation and thought and those who design or present courses and books for elementary and secondary schools. At the present speed of scientific discovery, reconstruction of conceptual frameworks, and application of scientific knowledge, those on the frontier cannot avoid increased responsibility for the effective dissemination of biological knowledge through formal courses and popular media, to young people and adults, to students directly and to their teachers."

6. "The rapidity of increase in knowledge requires both as much school as can be provided while not keeping youth from productive contributions any longer than is absolutely necessary, and continuing effort to find ways to condense and select what is taught so that the term of studentship is not extended indefinitely. Effort is needed to determine how some things now taught at more advanced levels can be learned at more elementary levels."

7. There is a need to recognize that biology has certain special problems. "Its objects are more difficult and elusive to study than some of those of other sciences," and the field is highly diversified. Biological education requires more coordination of special interests and programs than has typically occurred in the past.

The discussants felt that the following issues should be considered in devising an action program:

1. "The first task is to determine what biological knowledge can and should be learned at each school level; to define objectives and content."

2. "Account should be taken of differing capacities of slow, average and bright students; differing education goals; differing interests and enthusiasms of competent teachers, and differing local situations."

3. "The proportion of time that can fairly be claimed for science, and, within science, for biology at each level should be ascertained, taking account of time need for other subjects, ability and goals. The sequential relationships of science topics and areas should also be defined."

4. "After the shape of the biology teaching job at each school level is determined, needed instructional materials should be developed."

5. "These endeavors should pool the talents of different people and organizations." Professional associates, scientists, teachers, school administrators and others working in teams or singly should be involved according to the different competences required.

6. "Instructional programs and materials should be tested in selected schools, revised according to experience, tested and revised several times, if need be, and finally made available for general use by schools and in teacher education."

The committee proposed a specific program of biological education to serve as a basis for further deliberation by interested and qualified persons. The program identified the following series of projects for biological education in elementary and secondary schools:

1. A syllabus and study guide in biology for elementary teachers.

2. The development of a handbook on essential biology which students should obtain in high school, covering basic principles, concepts, facts, illustrative examples, documentation of ideas, and implications.

3. "The writing of short booklets on special topics in biology to supply background information for teachers on certain fields unfamiliar to many (genetics, cellular biology, etc.) or about applications and other special topics (biology of crop plants and cultivation, etc.), or booklets for students in advanced courses and other special situations."

4. The production of more laboratory and field studies for secondary school biology, along the line of those in *Laboratory and Field Studies in Biology: A Sourcebook for Secondary Schools.*
5. A study of equipment and materials important for the study of modern biology.
6. The production of film and television presentations that may serve to broaden student experiences in some phases of biology and save teaching time in other instances.
7. A study of the use of terminology in biology both to clarify terms and to reduce the unnecessary vocabulary.

In 1955 an *Education and Professional Recruitment Committee* was appointed by the American Institute of Biological Sciences and charged with the development of a program of biological education at all school levels. It was proposed that a comprehensive curriculum project be developed to include new course content, laboratory manuals, and teacher aids; the production of films, film strips, charts and models; a study of present in-service training of teachers; and the possible production of pamphlets, booklets, and other publications that may serve to increase the effectiveness of biological education. Oswald Tippo, Colorado University, was chairman of the AIBS Education Committee.

The steering committee for the various projects was composed of research biologists, high school biology teachers, educators and school administrators. H. Bentley Glass of Johns Hopkins University was chairman of the steering committee and Arnold B. Grobman, Florida State Museum, was appointed director of the Biological Sciences Curriculum Study. John A. Moore, Columbia University, was chairman of the Committee on the Content of the Curriculum and Addison E. Lee, University of Texas, chairman of the Committee on Innovations in Laboratory Instruction.

At the onset of the AIBS project the point of view was that resource materials to assist teachers should be produced rather than a definitive course of study. The ultimate purpose of the project was a biology program "which would, ideally, impart to the students those major biological principles which every educated person should know." The committee assumed that whatever curriculum materials were to be produced should result from the cooperative efforts of biologists, biology teachers, educators and school administrators with the assistance of those specially competent for a particular project.

The AIBS education programs were formulated with the following objectives in mind:

1. A knowledge of science is an important aspect of the thinking and philosophy of individuals.
2. The teaching of biology should include the intellectual activities of the science itself.
3. Instruction in biology should:
   a. Develop an appreciation of the discipline.
   b. Acquaint students with career potentialities.
   c. Lead to an understanding of basic principles.
   d. Orient the student "in proper perspective with and in relationship to the other fundamental disciplines."
4. The presentation of biology must be in terms of the student-citizen and "what he must know to be able to lead a satisfying and productive life."

At this time (1960) the educational projects of AIBS are in varying stages of progress, none have reached the projected dates for completion. The following descriptions of each program represent a stage of development somewhat beyond preliminary planning:

The *Committee on the Content of the Curriculum* of the Biological Sciences Curriculum Study planned several biology courses around the following statements of objectives:

1. "Most curricular objectives of the study are those which have traditionally guided the teaching of biology in the American school." These may be summarized "as conveying to the student an appropriate private understanding of his own body, of the diversities and commonalities of organisms in general, of their relations to the environment, of the means

by which we and they are cared for and conserved, and of the organized structures of fact and concept through which biology organizes and guides its inquiries.

2. The materials and organizations developed to serve these aims are also to serve an additional purpose. Through time, we hope to convey a conception of biological science by which the student may identify vocational and avocational interests and master a literate discipline which will render reports of future scientific progress accessible to him. This means that the materials of classroom and laboratory will present biology as a science which is an ongoing, self-correcting and revisionary process as well as a body of currently warranted fact and theory" (78).

3. The specific objectives for biology teaching which have been tentatively accepted to serve as a guide in preparing the preliminary courses of study were (54):

   a. An understanding of man's own place in the scheme of nature; namely, that he is a living organism and has much in common with all living organisms.

   b. An understanding of his own body; its structure and function.

   c. An understanding of the diversity of life and of the interrelations of all creatures.

   d. An understanding of what man presently knows and believes regarding the basic biological problems of evolution, development, and inheritance.

   e. An understanding of the biological basis of many of the problems and procedures in medicine, public health, agriculture and conservation.

   f. An appreciation of the beauty, drama, and tragedy of the living world.

   g. An understanding of the historical development and examples of some of the concepts of biology to show that these are dependent on the contemporary techniques, technology, and the nature of society.

   h. An understanding of the nature of scientific inquiry; that science is an open-ended intellectual activity and what is presently 'known' or believed is subject to 'change without notice'; that the scientist in his work strives to be honest, exact, and part of a community devoted to the pursuit of truth; that his methods are increasingly exact and the procedures themselves are increasingly self-correcting."

During the summer of 1960 sixty writers, including high school biology teachers, research biologists, and educators wrote three versions of a general biology course including textbooks, laboratory manuals and teachers' guides. Three course versions of biology were produced because it was felt that within the context of the objectives there could be several approaches to the subject. Each version was organized around a conceptual theme intended to provide a balanced introduction to the study of biology. This approach was in contrast to many of the existing textbooks where there was an absence of integrative concepts that would give the student an understanding of the science of biology. In each text an effort was made to present the content in a manner that would lead young people to an understanding of the nature and value of science. Biology as a process of inquiry was emphasized rather than as an inventory of the conclusions of research.

The three experimental textbooks produced in the summer of 1960 at the BSCS writing conference were identified as the versions "green", "yellow" and "blue". While similar topics were often presented in each text the biological approach to them differed (3), (4), (2).

The *Green Version* of the biology textbooks was developed from an ecological point of view. It took the individual organism as the primary unit of study. "It is concerned with how these individuals are organized into populations, species, and communities; with what organisms do and how they do it. The volume starts with cycles of energy and materials in the biosphere. It turns, then, to such structural units as individuals, populations and communities. Populations are recognized as including a great diversity of different kinds of animals, plants and microorganisms, which we briefly survey in the next three chapters.

"After describing this taxonomic diversity, we look at ecological diversity, at the different kinds of communities on land, in fresh water, and in the seas. Geographical diversity, differences among the continents and oceans, is next considered. Then we go back in time to look at the history of life, at the interpretation of the record of the rocks: which faces us with the problem of evolution.

"The problem of evolution brings us to the cellular structure of organisms and then to genetics. The following chapters treat the physiology and development of plants and animals. Animal physiology leads directly to animal behavior—the relations of the parts to the functioning of the whole organism. We end by a look at the human animal in the perspective of his biological setting.

"The laboratory exercises have much more of an ecological approach than the other versions."

The *Green Version* of the biology textbook is divided into the following chapters:

1. The World About Us
2. Individuals, Populations and Communities
3. Animal Diversity
4. Plant Diversity
5. Microscopic Life
6. Life on Land
7. Life in Inland Waters
8. Life in the Seas
9. The Geography of Life
10. The History of Life
11. The Cell
12. Genetics
13. Plant Physiology and Development
14. Animal Physiology and Development
15. Animal Behavior
16. Man in Nature

"Since the classification of organisms is dealt with in a rather unsystematic way in the text" a synopsis of the major groups or organisms is given in an appendix under the title, *The Catalogue of Nature*. The production of the *Green Version* was under the supervision of Marston Bates of the University of Michigan.

The *Yellow Version* begins, as does the *Green,* with the whole organism but a genetic-evolution theme is used throughout the text. "This starting point is emphasized by its second and third chapters. Chapter 2 treats man as exemplar of the animal, treating him from a functional point of view and with a minimum of fine detail. The traditional major functions are treated system by system, rarely going below the organ level. Chapter 3 performs a similar service for the green plant, though with much more detail and variety of examples. By means of the variety of examples, it is also able to emphasize notions of evolution and adaptation as these are seen in the various examples."

"Chapter 4 departs abruptly from the levels of organism and organ to confront the student with the fundamental chemistry and dynamics of the living cell. Its detail does not consist, however, of a multiplication of names or of diverse examples of the subjects treated. Rather, it consists of the details of chemical action without which an understanding of 'being alive' is likely to be emptily verbal." The intricacies of DNA and RNA and ATP and so on, are presented with this idea in mind.

The content and emphasis of the remaining chapters is sufficiently clear from the Table of Contents:

1. A Preview of Biological Problems
2. The Biology of Man—An Introduction to the Animal
3. Biology of the Green Plant
4. Matter, Energy and Life
5. Microbiology
6. Diversity in the Animal Kingdom
7. Diversity in the Plant Kingdom
8. Genetics
9. Reproduction and Development
10. Evolution
11. Selected Topics in Biology

In the final chapter of the *Yellow Version* is found a discussion of biological problems of special importance to man, such as, population, resources, behavior, disease, race. John Moore of Columbia University supervised the writing team of the *Yellow Version*.

The *Blue Version* prepared under the guidance of Ingrith Deyrup of Barnard, uses a "linear" approach and organization to the study of biology. "It begins (after the introductory material) with the basis of life in the properties and organization of matter. It moves from there to the activities of these organisms as seen in the capture and use of energy. (Sections IV and V). From here, it moves to the organ level (Section VI) and from the organ level to the level of the whole organism and of populations. The climax consists of a treatment of certain open-ended biological problems which face man himself as a citizen of a socially organized community.

"The outstanding characteristic of the *Blue Version* lies in its concern for a consistent level of difficulty. Much attention has been given to simplicity of presentation and to the elimination of detail considered unnecessary for the kind of understanding to be expected of the young student whose primary interest does not lie in biology. The effort to maintain a consistent level of simplicity and generality has been entirely successful in almost all sections and chapters. Only in the treatment of genetics and evolution is there a demand on the student which might be considered above the demand required by other chapters. However, it is the subject matter itself, rather than the treatment of it, that is largely responsible."

The laboratory exercises for the *Blue Version* have an emphasis on scientific inquiry with experimental approaches. The laboratory is more sophisticated than it is in the other versions.

The table of contents for the experimental version of the *Blue* text was:

PART 1

    SECTION I.   Chapter 1. *THE BIOLOGIST LOOKS AT THE WORLD*

The *Committee on Innovation in Laboratory Instruction* was made two committees in the summer of 1960. The original committee, under the chairmanship of Addison E. Lee, University of Texas, concentrated upon the refinement of the "block" laboratory program. The second committee gave its attention to the development of laboratory materials to accompany each of the three versions of the BSCS text. H. Bentley Glass, Johns Hopkins University, was chairman of this committee.

Laboratory work in biology teaching had been under severe criticism for over a half-century. The *Committee on Innovation in Laboratory Instruction* sought a new perspective to the proper function of laboratory instruction in biology. The point of view adopted was written to be read by high school students. The statement follows:

"There are two major aims in studying any natural science. One aim, the lesser in importance, is to become acquainted with the significant scientific facts upon which rest the major concepts and theories of science. These are the ideas that have so profoundly altered our views of man's place in nature and have so tremendously enlarged human powers over the forces and resources of nature. In biology, this objective also includes a firsthand acquaintance with living organisms and the outstanding features of their lives.

"The other aim is indispensable to young scientists and non-scientists alike—to everyone who hopes to participate intelligently in the life of a scientific age which so constantly demands difficult decisions and real wisdom. This second objective is to know what science really is—to recognize its spirit and to appreciate its methods. Science is not magic, and a scientific civilization surely will not endure if most people of intelligence regard science as a sort of magic. It is a way—or a composite of many ways—of finding out reliable, confirmed knowledge about all natural phenomena. It is compounded of the observations of the human senses and the inferences and deductions that can be derived from such experiences. It is generated by inextinguishable human curiosity, and has no necessary connection with efforts to improve the circumstances of human life, although such fruits do arise from scientific labor more generally than in any other way. Honesty and integrity are also indispensable in the fabric of science.

"In former days, when modern science was getting under way, much scientific work was done in the field, where nature can be observed at firsthand—and indeed, much biological work must still be done in the field. However, as time passed, it became more and more apparent that more precise measurements and more accurate observations can be made in the laboratory, because the scientific worker can then so control conditions that a comparison can be made between situations that differ in only one significant respect. That was the beginning of experiment (the experiment of the single variable), which made possible such logical certainty in drawing a conclusion that it has become the preferred method of science, wherever possible. In the broad sense, wherever this method is employed, whether indoors or outdoors, there is the scientist's *laboratory*.

"Science is social, resting upon the labors of many men directed at a common problem. Where some fail, others succeed. Together they accomplish far more than even a genius working in lonely isolation is likely to achieve. What is more, any scientist today can build on the earlier as well as contemporary investigations of men of other races, tongues, and kinds of insight. This is because a spirit of free communication permeates science. But for communication to be effective in such matters, it must be clear and precise, no matter what language it is spoken or written in; and for communication to be permanent, it must of course be given form in printing, drawing, or the like, and published and circulated.

"All these things amount to saying one thing of prime significance. The laboratory is where the work of science is done, where its spirit lives within those who work there, where its methods are transmitted from one generation to the next. One does not really learn science from books, one learns science by asking nature the right questions. And the laboratory is the place where one learns most readily what questions can be asked fruitfully, and how they must be put. It is where one learns why science insists on precise measurements, accurate observations, and conciseness and clarity in communication.

"When used for teaching, the laboratory should reflect both of these primary aims, the illustrative and the investigatory, as they might be called. The first function was probably the principal one in mind when Thomas Henry Huxley and Louis Agassiz introduced the teaching laboratory in biology. Their insight was a simple one: seeing is believing. In teaching science one must appeal not to the authority of a teacher or a book; one looks squarely at the facts, at the infinitely varied phenomena of nature. The first function of the laboratory in teaching is to present the evidence from nature to illustrate the basis of our biological concepts. Now this function has been heavily emphasized in the past, to such an extent that students have come to spend most of their time watching demonstrations, looking through a microscope, dissecting animals or plants, learning names, labeling drawings—but rarely doing an experiment, in the sense of really investigating a problem, the answer to which is unknown. To give a proper emphasis to the second, or investigatory, side of the study of science, something entirely different is needed—the active participation of the learner in some real scientific investigation, and in some depth. To accomplish this, time is needed, and that time can only come from a reduction in the purely illustrative side of the work. However, some time can be saved if we attempt to learn scientific skills only when they are directly needed for the work at hand. This is what a working scientist does. If he needs to use radioisotopes in his investigations, he learns how to use them; if his problem does not clearly require the development of skill in the use of radioisotopes, he doesn't, for the present, concern himself about them. He remains confident that whenever he needs to use a certain skill in his work he can proceed to acquire it.

"In short, this manual has a dual purpose: both to see what should be seen, and also to learn how to investigate quite a variety of biological problems. The manual contains 'Exercises.' Some of these are studies in seeing nature. Some are problems to be solved. Still others are real experiments, true introductions to the scientific investigation of problems. A few—not many, because it is difficult to run before you learn to walk—are what a scientist calls 'research.' These are the investigations of problems the answers to which *nobody* knows—neither your teacher, nor the college professors, nor the writers of this or any other science books. In grappling with this last sort of 'exercise' you may be disappointed, for nature is a hard master and reveals her secrets only to those who are patient and careful, persistent to the point of obstinacy, and willing to spend time and energy without reckoning the cost. But if you succeed, you will experience one of life's prize moments—a mixture of the joy of creation, like that of a composer who has just put the last note upon his score, together with the exuberance of the explorer, who from his jungle peak looks over a vast ocean, never seen before, sparkling in the sun below and beyond.

"No matter how much you learn about the facts of science, you will never quite understand what makes science the force it is in human history, or the scientists the sorts of people they are, until you have shared with them such an experience.

"The laboratory is the scientist's workshop. Much reading and discussion are essential in science work, but it is in the laboratory that hypotheses are tested.

"During your study of biology you will spend considerable time in the laboratory. You will learn to use biological apparatus such as the microscope, the manometer, the incubator, the centrifuge, the autoclave (or a pressure cooker), and the balance. In some experiments you may work with small animals such as mice or guinea pigs, with microorganisms, or with plants, and you will need to learn the care of these organisms" (5).

The *Committee on Innovation in Laboratory Instruction* recognized the need for "something entirely different" in high school laboratory work if students were to acquire an understanding of the *investigatory function* of science (50). The concept of the *"block approach"* was developed. It seemed clear that the investigatory function of science as an objective of biology teaching would require active participation of the student "in real scientific investigation, and in some depth."

At the present time we have no definite knowledge of how long a period of work is needed to achieve this aim. In any case, we should forego our effort to parallel all lectures and class discussions by formal laboratory exercises on every aspect of the course, and should trouble ourselves to learn scientific skills only when they are directly needed for the work at hand. This is what a working scientist does. If he needs to use radioisotopes in his investigation, he learns how to use them; if his problem does not clearly require the development of a skill in the use of radioisotopes, he doesn't concern himself with them for the present. He remains confident that if he needs to use a certain skill in his work he can acquire it when it becomes necessary.

It is true that this type of experimental approach has never been entirely neglected in our laboratory teaching. The best teachers and planners have always done what they could to include a truly experimental approach to the sciences in their laboratory teaching. Such efforts have floundered on the practical difficulty of compressing an experimental approach to a problem into the confines of a single laboratory period, or at best a short sequence. For the very essence of the experimental approach is that it continues to press toward a solution of a problem until results are obtained, whether this requires weeks or months. The very nature of the attack is 'open ended.' Properly to pursue this objective we therefore need a block of uninterrupted, consecutive time of considerable magnitude—a period when the students can press forward their investigations without interruption by extraneous assignments, discussion of other topics, tests, and other sorts of conventional study.

From such reasoning we have arrived at the concept of laboratory experience organized into 'blocks,' each of several weeks' duration, and each dealing with a specific biological problem, such as photosynthesis in green plants or the genetics of a sexually reproducing organism, the composition of a community or the systematic relations of a particular group of organisms. For to achieve this objective we are no longer concerned about a student's general knowledge of our science, but rather with a reasonably penetrating exploration of one selected problem, in order to advance as rapidly as may be to the frontiers of existing knowledge. We propose to concentrate on just those skills, and only those skills, that are necessary for this purpose. We propose to lead the student swiftly but surely to the exploration of true unknowns. *During the 5 to 6-week period occupied by a 'block' no other work will be scheduled in the course.*

What is envisaged is definitely not individual project work such as students prepare for science fairs, but rather is planned as group study with standard-sized classes having the usual variance in ability. One might begin with an adaptation of the historical approach, the "case history" study advocated by James Bryant Conant for the sciences. A few classic experiments might disclose the parameters of the problem and acquaint students with the basic techniques necessary for the planned experimental attack. Time would have to be spent to teach the need for careful, quantitative observations and for accurate perceptions of relationships of form to function. Applications of inductive and deductive reasoning to the problem would be quite as important as the development of needed skills of manipulation. The importance of experimental controls would be demonstrated in practice. By working in teams, replicating a given experiment, and in groups of teams performing the same experiment with one condition changed at a time, the class will learn how to cooperate in scientific endeavor and to pool their results. They will learn what is meant by the validity and reliability of scientific conclusions in the face of variability in results. They will learn why scientific conclusions are always tentative, best expressed as probabilities, not certainties. They will learn to prize suspended judgment, 'the greatest triumph of the scientific mind.'

They will find out, only too clearly, how the failure of one person or team to do a good job to some extent spoils the results of the whole class. When two or more classes are doing the same experiments independently, a nice rivalry can develop between them in the effort to secure good data. Eventually, well within the five or six weeks of allotted time, the students would arrive at the frontiers of knowledge in the area of their problem, at least in regard to some particulars, and can begin to develop their own hypotheses and to devise experiments to test them. Each student receiving such training would participate in the thrill of the Scientific Revolution that is reshaping modern life, would come to distinguish science from superstition, and as future citizen would be prepared to act intelligently in the numerous ways in which a scientific attitude is needed.

We have assurance that this type of approach can be developed effectively in the high school and even at elementary grade levels. Certainly in the high school it can be tried out. More-

over, since it may well prove that a single such 'block' will suf-
fice to achieve the aim of acquainting the student with the nature of scientific investigation and to provide the feeling of
being a participant in it, it may be possible to assign different
classes of students to different blocks, conducted at different
times during the school term. With the predicted floods of students upon us, and the diminishing supply of qualified teachers,
some administrators are already urging that science courses (at
least for non-majors) be planned without any laboratory work
at all. The yield to such pleas of expediency may end in foisting
upon the public the very misconceptions about the nature of science we most desire to avoid. Here at least, in the form of the
new "block" plan, lies a way out of the difficulty. Let us separate
the illustrative and the investigatory functions of laboratory
programs, leave the first to the classroom and informal 'open'
laboratory, and emphasize the essential place of the second.
Granting that a year-long, extensive acquaintance with the nature of scientific investigation might be better than a single,
brief experience—the latter may nevertheless be invaluable and,
under the circumstances, all that we can reasonably provide for
the great generality of students. At least, the educational experiment seems worth making.

The BSCS *Committee on Gifted Students,* under the chairmanship of Paul F. Brandwein, The Conservation Foundation,
was concerned with the development of (14):

1. A 'paper' on the nature of the environment which fosters
   creative work in the secondary school.
2. A bibliography of papers on the nature of giftedness and
   creativity in science, with special attention to biology.
3. Summaries on promising programs for development of able
   students in biology.
4. A collection of research problems in biology for gifted students.

The point of view of the committee was "that inspired course
work is not enough; we believe the creative student of high
school biology needs to be under the gentle burden of inde-

pendent research so that he learns that answers are not always available in textbooks. He needs to see biology not only as a body of tested knowledge but as a way of increasing man's knowledge." To implement this program the committee obtained from several hundred research biologists a "prospectus for a piece of research that a very able high school student might accomplish in two to three years of work." During the summer of 1960 the Gifted Student Committee selected one hundred of the research prospectuses and prepared them for publication. Each was identified by a title and the name of the biologist who submitted it. The majority were organized as follows: a) background to the problem; b) statement of the problem; c) suggested approach; and d) useful references. Special techniques, possible pitfalls and related problems were also included in many of the research descriptions. The precise statement of the problem, a hypothesis and the design of the experiment were responsibilities given the student as well as the paper describing his investigation.

A *Teacher Preparation Committee,* with Joseph J. Schwab, University of Chicago, as chairman, was responsible for the development of plans for the pre-service and in-service training of biology teachers who would teach the new BSCS courses. During the summer of 1960 the committee produced a *Teacher's Commentary* (6) to accompany the three versions of the biology texts produced in the BSCS writing conference.

The *Teacher's Commentary* was developed with four ideas in mind:

1. It should contribute to the teacher's own effort to enlarge his conception of science and biology.
2. It should contribute to the teacher's knowledge of new developments in his field.
3. It should contribute to growth in our working conception of the aims and processes of science education.
4. It should provide suggestions and stimuli to devise and experiment with new ways of meeting day to day challenges of the classroom.

A significant innovation in this commentary was the attention given to the development of concepts about the nature and processes of science. It was assumed that for the best teaching of biology the teacher must have a clear understanding of what is meant by science and more particularly the *science* of biology. The first part of the commentary is therefore an essay on the nature of biological enquiry.

A series of "invitations to enquiry" were developed for use with students. The committee had in mind that:

> An ideal 'invitation to enquiry' is any individual or collective enterprise which engages the student himself in one of the critical or investigative activities which constitute scientific enquiry. There are many starting points and many aims for such an invitation. It may begin with a conclusion already known and try to build the kind of experimental investigation which would justify it. It might start with a conclusion and its supporting experiments and set out to discern the weakness, the doubts or the inevitable assumptions which are involved. It might start with a problem rather than a conclusion and try to construct an experimental design to solve it. It might be a much smaller undertaking, such as one which starts with data already collected and moves from them to a conclusion or interpretation.

The titles of some of the "invitations" developed were: "The Meaning of Classification"; "A Case of Conflicting Evidence"; "Cause and Correlation"; "A Pattern of Experimental Enquiry" and "On the Role of Assumption in Science."

The BSCS *Committee on Publication,* with Hiden T. Cox, Executive Director, American Institute of Biological Sciences, as chairman, has planned (1960) a series of pamphlets for use in biological education. It was anticipated that the pamphlets created would 1) assist teachers to keep current with new developments in biology, 2) provide authoritative readings on biological topics for the general public and 3) serve as a resource library in the schools. A single pamphlet would consider a specific biological topic, concept or summary of research.

In 1957 the Education Committee of the AIBS recommended

making a series of biological films for use in the secondary schools. A steering committee of fifteen members was appointed with representation from research biologists, high school biology teachers, science educators and school administrators. Oswald Tippo, Colorado University, was ex officio chairman of the committee. H. Burr Roney, University of Houston, was appointed director of the *Secondary School Biological Sciences Film Series* (77). Over 200 consultants, mostly professional biologists and high school biology teachers, participated in creating and evaluating the 120 films in the series.

The film project was designed to present a course in biology at the tenth grade level through a series of 30-minute lecture-demonstration films. The content of the course was designed to treat ten major topics of biology with twelve films planned on each of the following topics:

1. Cell biology
2. Microbiology
3. Multicellular plants
4. Multicellular animals
5. Reproduction, growth and development
6. Genetics
7. The diversity of plants
8. The diversity of animals
9. Ecology
10. Life, time and change

The various topics were brought into a degree of unity through the use of continuing integrative themes, which were, 1) homeostasis; 2) evolution; 3) ecology; 4) the complementarity of structure and function; 5) man's role in nature (biological problems); 6) methods (the process of "sciencing" as a human activity; and 7) behavior as a biological phenomenon, with adaptive significance.

A Teacher's Manual and a Study Guide were developed to assist in relating classwork and the film series. The Teacher's Manual included "background material to aid the teacher, reference sources, topic outlines of the films, including possible film stop points, and suggested discussion subjects for those points and others, suggestions for field and lab work, etc."

Many efforts to improve the teaching of biology as a whole or in particular aspects were made during the 1950–1960 decade. Professional societies, educational groups, foundations and organizations of biology teachers produced curriculum and resource materials for use in the high school.

The *Committee on Education of the Society of American Bacteriologists* prepared descriptive course materials, laboratory experiments, audio-visual aids, and student and teacher bibliographies for use in teaching microbiology in the high school (7).

The Science Manpower Project of Teachers College, Columbia University developed and published in 1959 a course on *Modern High School Biology* (81). The course was designed specifically to fit into a sequence of science offerings extending from the junior high school through the senior high school, and with the intent of avoiding the many duplications in content usually found in general science and biology. By moving simpler biological materials into general science, a more substantial course at the tenth grade level was found to be possible.

The National Association of Biology Teachers prepared a comprehensive *Handbook for Teaching Conservation and Resource-Use Education* (83). The project was supported by the *American Nature Association* and developed by the *National Conservation Committee* of the National Association of Biology Teachers. Richard L. Weaver, University of Michigan, was chairman of the committee and project leader. The handbook was designed not as a text but as a guide "to some of the outstanding examples of good conservation teaching in the United States. The Handbook contains many examples and illustrates the great variety of useful and successful methods and techniques available to the teacher of conservation and resource-use."

In 1959, the National Association of Biology Teachers prepared a *Manual for Outdoor Laboratories* (84). This publication contains suggestions and examples for "the development and use of school grounds as outdoor laboratories for teaching science and conservation."

The *Conservation Foundation* through its Editorial Board for Teaching Science Through Conservation, sponsored the publication of a textbook on *Teaching Science Through Conservation* (56). The authors of the text, Martha E. Munzer and Paul E. Brandwein, were members of The Conservation Foundation Staff. While the publication was described as a textbook it was the intention of the foundation not to consider conservation as a separate subject, "but rather as an integral part of science teaching." The approach is one that "emphasizes the interrelationship between conservation and the many branches of science —general science, biology, chemistry, and physics."

The participants of the *National Conference for High-School Biology Teachers* held at the University of Chicago, November 24–28, 1959, developed a pamphlet considering the teaching of evolution in the high school (53). "The conference was an outgrowth of the planning for the Darwin Centennial Celebration and was designed to enable outstanding high-school science teachers to think together with outstanding scientists about the improvement of high-school instruction in science" particularly in regard to "the broad relevance of the concept of evolution in modern thinking. It led also to a clearer realization of the problems involved in incorporating modern concepts into the teaching of high-school biology." *Using Modern Knowledge to Teach Evolution in High School* is a summary of the thoughts of the participants in the conference, and was prepared by John C. Mayfield, University of Chicago.

During the last half of the 1950–1960 decade there was much local school activity in producing new biology curricula. Particular interest was shown in the development of advanced courses for those students with a special interest in biology. Characteristically, the advanced work included more biochemistry, radiochemistry, and biophysics than elementary courses. A first year college textbook in general biology was usually the basis for the actual course taught. Elementary biology, chemistry and sometimes physics were made prerequisites for the advanced course.

Another curriculum pattern that found favor was the "senior seminar" or "junior research" program. Here the student carried on a minor research study for an extended period of time, sometimes for a year on a single problem. Whether the problem was biological in nature was dependent upon the interests of the student. The "seminar" arrangement was particularly suited to smaller schools where the enrollment for advanced work in science justified only a single general course. Research biologists were frequently used as consultants in these programs.

A few schools moved the tenth grade biology course into the ninth grade. The course content remained that of the tenth grade offering, but at the ninth grade level the subject became an "advanced biology." The rationale for the movement was to make it possible for science-interested students to carry four years of college preparatory science in high school.

Summary 1950–1960

The educational controversies of the fifties reflected the scientific revolution, characterized by an "explosion of knowledge", and the changes in the larger scheme of cultural values in America. Demands for scientific and technically trained manpower found a serious imbalance in the supply-demand ratio of scientists. Pressures were then brought to bear for a rethinking of the goals of education in the sciences. The plea was for "quality", "excellence" or "rigor" in high school science courses. Precise definitions of what those attributes meant for the curriculum in science were lacking.

The literature on science teaching for this period was extensive and controversial. A representative bibliography on the major issues and problems is listed at the end of this chapter. In the selection of references, preference was given to symposia, committee and commission reports. The Committee on Educational Policies of the Division of Biology and Agriculture of the National Academy of Sciences–National Research Council, in 1957, published a comprehensive survey of the literature on biological education, including reports on conferences, institutes, committees, and special studies. This bibliography is a selection of published articles covering the period from 1920 to 1955. The reader with an interest in the modern movements in secondary school science education will find these two bibliographies of special value.

The first high school course to be reorganized during the 1950–1960 period was physics, followed next by chemistry. The curriculum committees sought to remove much of the technological, add more "science", reduce the number and update concepts in the courses. New laboratory experiments were devised that were more in terms of the nature of science. These courses were designed for the fraction of the high school population that ordinarily elect physics and chemistry.

The biology curriculum committees developed their courses for the typical tenth grader. Their efforts were to develop a more integrated course built around an interpretative theme, such as ecology, evolution, or energy exchange. The "atomic era" and the "space age" had an influence on the high school biology course. Teaching units on "radiation biology" and "space biology" were added to biology textbooks and courses of study. Conservation education had a renewed emphasis. Advanced biology, a second year of biology, was popular in the larger schools. Frequently "advanced course" meant using a college biology textbook in high school.

The need to improve the laboratory work in biology received much attention. Most of the recommendations were for a more experimental approach to the study of biology. This was in contrast to the passive observation of non-living organisms so typical of biology teaching. The plea for more field work and the study of living organisms continued in much the same vein as that made by biology curriculum committees for the past half century. The difference was that the more recent committees devised and published examples of improved experiments.

Teaching resources, such as films, pamphlets and booklets

were produced to assist in the improvement of science teaching. The extent to which these resources will be used can be only postulated at this time.

Possibly the most conspicuous educational activity of the past five years has been the willingness of the research scientist to work on instructional materials at the pre-college level. From 1890 to 1920 the university biologists were active members, and usually in the majority, on practically all national and regional curriculum committees. Although individual biologists have since acted as textbook consultants, respondents to curriculum questionnaires and as teacher institute speakers, they have had little direct involvement in the improvement of high school biological education.

Special interest has been shown in the development of teaching materials better suited to the gifted student or rapid learner. Mostly these have been in the nature of "research" projects that would provide the student with an intellectual challenge.

The National Defense Education Act passed by Congress in 1958 made it possible for elementary and secondary schools to purchase additional laboratory equipment and reference books. The American Association for the Advancement of Science established a plan for providing, on loan, complete science libraries to schools. Lists of inexpensive science books were also published. The Atomic Energy Commission established a traveling-science-teacher program to give demonstrations and lectures in the smaller high schools. The American Institute of Biological Sciences made it possible for research biologists from universities to visit secondary schools. Nearly all the professional scientific societies published career bulletins for use in high school classes. Summer, year-long and in-service teacher education programs were sponsored by the National Science Foundation in various colleges and universities. Similar plans were supported by private foundations and industry. Science fairs and seminars were used to stimulate interest in science and to bring high school students into direct contact with scientists. Teachers were employed by universities and in industrial research laboratories to provide them with experience in research. These activities are illustrative of the massive effort made to improve the teaching of science in the schools between 1950 and 1960.

There was considerable activity in the development of new teacher training programs in science. The appropriateness of the training needed to teach a modern course in high school biology was explored. Experimental teacher education programs were designed to evaluate some of the many suggestions. It is too early to be able to report the significance of these studies. Major unresolved problems were the scarcity of young people who wish to make high school science teaching a career and the number who leave the profession each year.

The 1960–1970 decade began with a series of new biology courses, laboratory experiments and teaching resources. During the school year 1960–1961 over 14,000 students in 110 high schools were experimenting with a new biology course developed by the Biological Sciences Curriculum Study. Some preliminary work was under way to study the place of biology in the curriculum from the first grade through high school. While new courses had been developed by 1961 in each of the sciences —biology, chemistry, and physics—but little attention had been given to a correlated plan of education in the sciences at the high school level.

There is no real way to judge the extent to which the biology curriculum committees, for the seventy-year period covered by this study, were effective in bringing about changes in either the content or conduct of biology courses. It is apparent that the ideas for the improvement of biology teaching being discussed today are quite similar to many of those suggested before the turn of the century. One would find it difficult to date or to place in sequence the committee efforts of the past if they were not identified by year of publication or membership. Yet, there have been changes in biology teaching. Only a small fraction of these, however, directly reflect the specific recommendations of an identifiable committee. Sometimes the suggestions of a committee did not appear to bear fruit until a half century later; witness the consistent efforts to make laboratory work "a study of living organisms," and to have courses focus on the significant concepts of biology. Nearly every committee recommended that more attention be given the nature of science in biology teaching, but there is little of this to be found even today in textbooks or classrooms.

An analysis of the factors involved in getting curriculum reforms into the educational stream and to the point where they have an impact on the education of the student is sorely needed. Several hypotheses may be made about the ineffectiveness of biology curriculum committees in the past. There are limitations on the extent to which these can be analyzed for the purposes of this study, but these are some of the components of the problem:

1. The educational and social concepts underlying the need for a curriculum change were never made clear by recommending committees. Therefore, the classroom teacher was placed in the position of accepting a change without an adequate explanation of its necessity. In other words, there was an absence of theory to give meaning to the new program. It is paradoxical that a committee of scientists would find no need for theory to direct or interpret the initiation of an experimental program.

2. The new courses were simply outlined in a few pages and the teaching content was not developed to a point where the teacher could take over.

3. There was a failure to consider the entire teaching process—curriculum, class techniques, evaluation, laboratory work, and teacher education. An adequate theory of learning was rarely considered and the research on learning was not utilized in curriculum development. The result was that the "new" curriculum was nearly always no more effective than the old.

4. University biology departments did not assume the responsibility for the development of a program suitable for the training of secondary school biology teachers, nor did the

faculty counsel the better students toward a career in high school teaching.

5. The committees were not able to make the results of their work known to any appreciable number of high school biology teachers, university biologists, or school administrators.

6. The curriculum recommendations were usually more suited to the small minority of students who might continue into college and become biologists, and were not conceived in terms of developing a biological literacy on the part of all young people.

7. None of the committees established a program of educational research needed to resolve the many problems inherent in a curriculum reorganization.

The program of the Biological Sciences Curriculum Study of the American Institute of Biological Sciences was designed to overcome the majority of the inadequacies of previous committees.

BIBLIOGRAPHY ON PROBLEMS AND ISSUES IN SCIENCE EDUCATION, 1950–1960

Secondary School Education

American Association of School Administrators. 1958. *The High School in a Changing World.* National Education Association, Washington, D. C. 383 p.

Chase, Francis S. and Anderson, Harold A., Editors. 1958. *The High School in a New Era.* (Papers presented at the Conference on the American High School at the University of Chicago, October, 1957) The University of Chicago Press. 465 p.

Conant, James B. 1959. *The American High School Today.* McGraw-Hill Company, Inc., New York. 140 p.

Koerner, James D. 1959. The Case for Basic Education. Little, Brown, Co., Boston, 256 p.

The Educational Policies Commission. 1958. *The Contemporary Challenge to American Education.* National Education Association, Washington, D. C. 31 p.

America at Mid-Century Series. 1958. *The Pursuit of Excellence—Education and the Future of America.* Panel Report V of the Special Studies Project. Doubleday & Company Inc., Garden City. 49 p.

The Educational Policies Commission. 1956. *Manpower and Education.* National Education Association, Washington, D. C. 128 p.

The Educational Policies Commission. 1959. *An Essay on Quality in Public Education.* National Education Association, Washington, D. C. 29 p.

Rickover, H. G. 1959. *Education and Freedom.* E. P. Dutton & Company, Inc., New York. 256 p.

Symposia on Science Education

A.I.B.S. *Bulletin.* 1959. Special Issue, "An AIBS Education Program Emerges" 9(2):1:23.

Barnard, J. Darrell, Chairman. 1960. *Rethinking Science Education.* The Fifty-ninth Yearbook of the National Society for the Study of Education, Part I. University of Chicago Press, Chicago. 344 p.

Bulletin of the Atomic Scientist. 1958. Special Issue, "Science and Education." 14:345–384.

The Bulletin of the National Association of Secondary Principals. 1960. Special Issue, "Quality Science in Secondary Schools." 44(260):3:211.

Daedalus. 1959. Special Issue, "Education in the Age of Science." 88:1–205. Also in book form. Blanshard, Brand, Editor. 1959. *Education in the Age of Science.* Basic Books. N. Y. 302 p.

Elbers, Gerald W. and Duncan, Paul, Editors. 1959. *The Scientific Revolution—Challenge and Promise.* (Published in Cooperation with the President's Committee on Scientists and Engineers) Public Affairs Press. Washington, D. C. 280 p.

Fitzpatrick, Frederick L., Editor. 1960. *Policies for Science Education.* Bureau of Publications, Teachers College, Columbia University. 219 p.

Roucek, Joseph S., Editor. 1959. *The Challenge of Science Education.* Philosophical Library, New York. 491 p.

Teacher Education

American Association for the Advancement of Science and American Association of Colleges for Teacher Education. 1960. *Improving Science and Mathematics in Secondary Schools.* (A Report of the Joint Commission on the Education of Teachers of Science and Mathematics) AAAS or AACTE, Washington, D. C. 41 p.

National Education Association. 1958. *The Education of Teachers: New Perspectives.* (Papers and official group reports of the Second Bowling Green Conference) National Commission on Teacher Education and Professional Standards, Washington, D. C. 399 p.

National Education Association. 1959. *The Education of Teachers: Curriculum Programs.* (Report of the Kansas TEPS Conference) National Commission on Teacher Education and Professional Standards. Washington, D. C. 453 p.

Report of Conference on Nationwide Problems of Science Teaching in the Secondary Schools. 1953. *Critical Years Ahead in Science Teaching.* Harvard University Press, Cambridge. 48 p.

Woodring, Paul. 1957. *New Directions in Teacher Education.* The Fund for the Advancement of Education, New York. 141 p.

The Academically Talented Student

Brandwein, P. E. 1955. *The Gifted Student as Future Scientist.* Harcourt, Brace, New York. 107 p.

Cole, Charles C., Jr. 1956. *Encouraging Scientific Talent.* College Entrance Examination Board, New York. 259 p.

Conant, James B., Chairman. 1958. *The Identification and Education of the Academically Talented Student in the American Secondary School.* The Conference Report, National Education Association, Washington, D. C. 160 p.

Donaldson, Robert R., Chairman. 1959. *Science for the Academically Talented Student in the Secondary School.* (Report of conference sponsored by the NEA Project on Academically Talented Students and the National Science Teachers Association) National Science Teachers Association, Washington, D. C. 63 p.

Special Bulletins

President's Science Advisory Committee. 1959. *Education for the Age of Science.* U. S. Government Printing Office, Washington, D. C. 36 p.

National Science Foundation. 1960. *Statistical Handbook of Science Education.* U. S. Government Printing Office, Washington, D. C. 94 p.

National Academy of Sciences—National Research Council. 1957. *Biological Education, A Partial Bibliography.* Publication 518. NAS-NRC. Washington, D. C. 157 p.

Learning Science

Bruner, Jerome S. 1960. *The Process of Education.* (Report of the Woods Hole Conference) Harvard University Press, Cambridge. 97 p.

Mills, Lester C., Dean, Peter M. 1960. *Problem Solving Methods in Science Teaching.* Science Manpower Project Monographs. Bureau of Publications, Teachers College, Columbia University. 88 p.

Soviet Education

DeWitt, Nicholas. 1955. *Soviet Professional Manpower, Its Education, Training and Supply.* National Science Foundation, U. S. Government Printing Office, Washington, D. C. 400 p.

Hechinger, Fred M. 1959. *The Big Red Schoolhouse.* Doubleday & Company, Inc., New York. 240 p.

Korol, Alexander G. 1957. *Soviet Education for Science and Technology.* Massachusetts Institute of Technology and John Wiley & Sons, New York. 513 p.

Counts, George S. 1957. *The Challenge of Soviet Education.* McGraw-Hill Book Company, Inc., New York. 329 p.

U. S. Department of Health, Education, and Welfare. 1958. *Education in the USSR.* Bulletin 1957, No. 14. Government Printing Office, Washington, D. C. 226 p.

Science Education in Great Britain

Ministry of Education Pamphlet No. 38. 1960. *Science in Secondary Schools.* Her Majesty's Stationery Office, London. 164 p.

Perkins, W. H. 1958. *Science in Schools.* (Proceedings of a Conference under the auspices of the British Association for the Advancement of Science) Butterworths Scientific Publications, London. 150 p.

PART II

RESEARCH STUDIES

IX

Books on the Teaching of Secondary School Biology

THE REPORTS of curriculum committees represent one effort to improve the teaching of high school biology. A few biologists have taken the teaching of the subject as a problem for study and investigation. Typically these men have sought to summarize the current thinking and investigations on biology teaching, and then, in light of their own teaching experience, to suggest procedures and techniques for presenting biology to students. These books are primarily addressed to beginning teachers.

Comparatively few books have been written specifically on the teaching of biology. Books published early in this century advocated the values of a particular biological science, such as, William F. Ganong's, *The Teaching Botanist,* published in 1899 with a second edition in 1910; and F. E. Lloyd and M. A. Bigelow's *The Teaching of Biology in the Secondary School,* published in 1904. Lloyd and Bigelow's book was divided into two sections, the first part on the teaching of botany and nature study, and the second part on the teaching of zoology including human physiology. Neither book attempted to present a unified picture of biology, but then this was not a widely accepted point of view at that time.

Between 1934 and 1939 four books on the teaching of biology were published. Since that time there have been books on the teaching of conservation and laboratory sourcebooks for general biology courses but none that attempted to present a comprehensive view of biological education. In high school science methods books a separate chapter may sometimes be found on the special problems of biology teaching.

A purpose for considering the works of individual authors is that they endeavor to consider the teaching of biology in all of its aspects; purposes, curriculum, laboratory work, teaching procedures, learning resources and evaluation. The reports of committees, on the other hand, are more likely to consider only one phase of teaching, typically curriculum content.

In the selections that follow the major ideas of the writers who have published books on biology teaching are summarized and categorized. The books represented are:

1. Cole, William E. 1934. *The Teaching of Biology*. D. Appleton-Century Co. New York. 252 p.
2. Kinsey, Alfred C. 1937. *Methods in Biology*. J. P. Lippincott Co., Chicago. 279 p.
3. Miller, David F. and Blaydes, Glenn W. 1938. *Methods and Materials for Teaching Biological Sciences*. McGraw-Hill Co., Inc. 435 p.
4. Wells, Harrington. 1936. *The Teaching of Nature and the Biological Sciences*. The Christopher Publishing House. Boston. 342 p.

The authors had areas of agreement and disagreement on every phase of high school biology teaching.

A. On the purposes for teaching biology.
   1. There was unanimous agreement that:
     a. Secondary school biology must place its emphasis upon effective living in contemporary society.
     b. Biology should be taught as a method of thinking as well as an accumulation of knowledge.
     c. Biology teaching should place a greater emphasis upon the social implications of science and the impact of science upon social change.
     d. The teaching of biology should provide a background of knowledge that will enable the student to think on the subject.
   2. Half of the writers agreed that:
     a. Biology teaching should change to meet changes in society, educational thinking and new developments in biology.
     b. Biology teaching should be oriented toward better citizenship.

    c. Biology teaching should be of a practical nature with an emphasis upon the consumer aspects of the subject.

3. Only one author subscribed to each of the following purposes:

    a. Biology teaching should relate to the broad problems of everyday living with the course content drawn from the other sciences as needed to understand the problem.

    b. Biology teaching should focus on the Cardinal Principles of Education.

    c. Biology teaching should prepare students for both immediate and future living.

The position of the authors with regard to "why teach biology" varied between a concept of liberal education and education for the specialist. Most agreed that one value in studying biology is to learn something of the methodology of science. There was unanimous recognition that the student should develop an understanding of biology in relation to social and economic problems. However, it was apparent that the authors did not want high school biology to be either a "social biology" or a "human biology."

B. The learning of biology.

1. There was a general agreement that the following principles of learning were important in the study of biology:

    a. The teacher should utilize student interests to maximize learning.

    b. Some logical organization of the course is essential for effective learning.

    c. Learning material should be of sufficient variety to provide for individual differences.

    d. The learning situations should be similar to those found in everyday life.

    e. The effectiveness of learning is indicated by the student's ability to use his knowledge for solving problems found in everyday living.

    f. Learning is understanding and not an accumulation of facts.

    g. Learning depends upon the organization of facts until a relationship is seen and understood.

    h. Accurate learning depends upon accurate observation.

There was agreement among the biologists that "applications to daily living" improve the learning of biology. While all of the writers agreed that the real measure of effectiveness in learning is indicated by the student's ability to use his knowledge, and that facts alone would not accomplish this result, the idea of concepts and principles as outcomes of instruction was not clearly supported. Student motivation was recognized to be important and was assumed to be inherent in the nature of course content. In terms of what was generally known about learning theory at the time these books were written, suggestions for teaching were frequently in contradiction to the research in the field.

    C. The specific objectives for teaching biology.
        1. There was unanimous agreement on the following objectives:
            a. To develop an understanding of the methods of science and the ability to use these methods in the solutions of problems.
            b. To develop those scientific attitudes or habits of thinking which will contribute to a better adjustment of the individual.
            c. To promote the acquisition of worthwhile information.
        2. For each of the following objectives, three out of four of the books were in agreement:
            a. To develop an understanding of the nature and organization of the environment.
            b. To develop interests which will lead to leisure time activities.
            c. To develop an understanding of the principles of science which may function directly in the life of the student.

The biologists saw the major outcome of biology teaching to be a knowledge of biological phenomena. They would place less emphasis upon such topics as health, conservation, and biology in world affairs. All of the authors were in agreement that the "methods of science" should be emphasized in teaching biology.

    D. The content of the biology course.
        1. The following criteria for the selection of course content were accepted by all of the authors:

     a. The content should appeal to the interests of the students.
     b. The content should be related to the local community.
     c. The content should contribute to the aims of science teaching.
  2. Three out of four of the books cited the following criteria:
     a. The content selected should be of a nature that firsthand learning activities can be utilized.
     b. The content should represent a proper distribution of the subject fields of biology.

The biologists disagreed on using the following criteria for the selection of course content: material of wide human or social value; materials related to the specific needs of students; materials useful simply for the purpose of developing new interests; and materials that might be useful to coordinate or integrate all the sciences. Some of the authors considered these criteria of secondary importance. Biologists tend to stress the importance of getting a "proper distribution" of subject content in high school biology courses. Essentially this means a balance of content from the botanical and zoological fields.

  E. The organization of course content.
    1. The biologists were in agreement that students should not participate in the organization of the course.
    2. Most of the authors would like to have the biology course organized around problems.
    3. Half of the writers saw the possibility of organizing the course around the major principles of biology.
    4. Some authors wanted the biology course to parallel related content in the social studies.
    5. None were of the opinion that a textbook should be the sole guide to the organization of a course.

It is evident that there was little agreement about the proper way to organize a high school biology course. The emphasis upon an organization around *problems* or *principles* implies a search for an integrative theme to provide a biological unity to the content.

  F. The methods of teaching high school biology.

1. The biologists were in agreement that:
   a. There is no *one* method that is suitable for all teaching situations.
   b. The method should depend upon the objective sought.
2. The majority agreed that:
   a. Field trips and excursions, well-planned as to purpose, are valuable teaching procedures.
   b. Much class time should be spent in the application of biological principles to new situations.
3. Half of the authors were of the opinion that:
   a. A wide variety of reading references should be used in the biology course.
   b. Demonstrations should be used more frequently.
   c. A problem solving approach is an effective way of teaching.
   d. Students should seek information from a variety of sources, including museums, zoos, resource speakers, etc.

In contradiction to the educational trends of the time the biologists were not enthusiastic about the following teaching procedures:

1. Supervised study.
2. The use of films.
3. Student self-directive learning procedures.

There was little agreement as to how biology laboratory work should be organized; only half of the authors supported any single idea.

G. The nature of biology laboratory work.
   1. The most frequently mentioned ideas were that the work in the laboratory should:
      a. Have an experimental aspect to it.
      b. Be closely related to class activities.
      c. Relate to the objectives of biology teaching.
      d. Require analytical rather than representative drawings.
      e. Cultivate habits of accurate observation.
      f. Use laboratory drawings to fix in the minds of the students the facts to be learned.
      g. Provide training in the skills essential for good experimentation.

    h. Be planned and organized by the teacher.
    i. Require orderliness and cleanliness.
    j. Require laboratory notebooks to hold pupils properly responsible for laboratory work.

The writers were not particularly concerned with the ways in which the results of laboratory work would be used, the nature of the "write-ups", or the length of the laboratory period.

H. The nature of testing and evaluation in biology courses.
    1. The following items had the strongest support:
        a. Tests should indicate the extent to which the objectives of science teaching are achieved.
        b. Tests should help to diagnose the educational strengths and weaknesses of students.
        c. Tests can serve as a motivating device.
        d. Tests should require students to select, analyze, and organize data.
        e. Tests should be short and administered frequently.

Only one of the four books recommended the use of tests to indicate: 1) the student's understanding and ability to apply the principles of biology; 2) the application of biological knowledge to specific problems; 3) the status of laboratory achievement; 4) the student's growth in the achievement of "scientific attitudes." While there was agreement that tests should measure achievement in the objectives of a course, any specific suggestions for evaluating particular objectives were lacking.

Summary

There is not extensive agreement among the authors of textbooks on biology teaching about the purposes or methods of teaching high school biology. Each writer analyzed the problems, made an interpretation and formulated recommendations that seemed appropriate to him. The disagreements among the authors and the frequent inconsistency of a writer with his own assumptions suggest that the place of biology in a liberal education is not clearly defined. Objectives were stated that could not be achieved by the teaching procedures that were outlined and motivating devices were recommended that have not proved successful.

The question of how biology as a *science* might be presented in a course for high school students was not made clear. The biologists, judging from the authors reviewed, had difficulty in synthesizing the field sufficiently to develop a year course for high school students that would represent the biological sciences or encompass the nature of living substances. The biologists were inclined to view the subject in terms of naming parts, associating functions, and identifying species. They were not inclined to consider student or adult interests in course development. More attention was given to the logic of the subject matter and a balance of content among the various fields of biology.

As a group the biologists rejected the idea that biology should be an accumulation of isolated facts; but at the same time they did not support a conceptual organization of biology courses in terms of principles, concepts, laws or other integrating themes. They accepted in general the organization of a course around biological problems, but not if these meant problems of an "applied" nature, such as conservation, health, or improving agriculture. There seemed to be little awareness of the research on the nature of learning, the investigations on science teaching, or the recommendations of professional scientific societies that were interested in the improvement of science teaching.

No books reviewing biological education as a whole have been published since 1938, although there have been sourcebooks and handbooks on biology laboratory work and several works on the teaching of conservation. The most recent work on the teaching of biology, although still in an experimental form, is the *Teacher's Commentary* for the various text versions of the Biological Sciences Curriculum Study.

X

Investigations on the Objectives of High School Biology

THE IMPROVEMENT of the biology curriculum in high schools depends upon the development of a point of view consistent with the functions of secondary school education and the contributions of science to a liberal education. It must also be assumed that biology instruction has value for *all* young people. Then, for a smaller number of students there should be special opportunities. The work of the biology committees described in the earlier chapters of this study comprise efforts to establish these perspectives.

The selection of course content, with its management and presentation, has been the subject of research directed toward maximizing the teaching and learning processes of biology. Once the objectives for science teaching are established the problem becomes that of finding teaching practices that are effective, efficient and economical in terms of the learning outcomes that are sought. These problems represent the majority of the investigations on the teaching of science. Most of the research results have application to the teaching of biology, physics, or chemistry. In this study the majority of investigations cited were selected specifically for their pertinence to biology teaching and for their significance in curriculum development. Studies on course enrollments, local resources for biology teaching, teacher education, atypical student populations, and development of special resource units (conservation, health, anthropology and others), supervision of instruction and administration of science programs have been omitted.

Approximately 900 investigations on science teaching were examined and half were eliminated after a cursory examination for a lack of specificity to biology teaching. A total of 360 studies were abstracted; 100 studies with some likelihood of relevance were unobtainable. The studies reported were selected to provide a "picture" of curriculum research in the biological sciences. The paucity of studies on a particular problem is representative of the available research in this category.

Educational research like research in most fields is subject to fashions; this is illustrated by the high concentration of studies on a particular problem for a limited period of time, without later reference. It could also mean the questions appear to have been answered within present theory, or the techniques for obtaining further refinements are not available.

Studies on the Objectives for Teaching Biology

The question of objectives for the teaching of science is central to curriculum planning. Hurd (1954), in a sample of 3,133 statements written by high school science teachers over a fifty-year period (1901–1951), found that the objectives were their greatest concern. Educational objectives serve as hypotheses by means of which a biology teacher makes decisions about the curriculum, its organization and the selection of teaching procedures. Good teachers have reasons for the ways in which they work; these reasons are expressed in terms of educational objectives.

The concept of education in the sciences is influenced by new developments in biological knowledge; changes in learning theory; social, cultural, and economic developments; and public whims. A continuous rethinking of educational theory in the light of these developments is essential for the best kind of science education. To the same degree that progress in science is judged by its development of new theory in the light of new knowledge and increased understanding, the improvement of the educational enterprise demands a continuous restructuring of its philosophical assumptions.

The reports of the committees cited in the first part of this study give the *thinking* of different groups about the purposes for teaching biological science. Investigative studies on objectives are summarized in this section of the report.

The historical development of biology teaching objectives is reviewed in studies by Stout (1921); Finley (1926); Nelson (1928); Fay (1930); Christy (1936); Hurd (1949); Rosen (1955) and (1959). These investigations, using a variety of data, show modifications in the objectives for the teaching of biological subjects over the past century. Studies upon the objectives accepted by science teachers have been frequent. Hunter (1910) surveyed 276 high schools representing 34 states to determine the direction of emphasis teachers actually gave to their courses. He found this to be in the following areas of biology: human physiology, 178; morphology, 139; human welfare, 138; ecology, 136; natural history, 106; taxonomy, 19. This survey revealed a decided emphasis on health and human biology. Hunter (1932) continued his study of objectives for science teaching with a sampling of 393 widely distributed high schools. His results were expressed in terms of total percent of teachers stressing each obective: 1) propaedeutic functions, 19%; 2) to give information, 12%; 3) to master scientific method, 11%; 4) to understand the environment, 10%; 5) to develop skill in doing useful tasks, 10%; 6) to establish habits of scientific thinking, 9%; 7) to arouse interest in science, 7%; 8) to develop a scientific attitude toward all problems, 5%; 9) to gain a knowledge of the environment, 3%; 10) to appreciate value of health, 3%; 11) to explore pupils' interests, 3%; 12) to develop powers, 2%; 13) to arouse interest in environment, 2%; 14) to develop an appreciation of the work of scientists, 2%; 15) to explore the field of science, 1%; 16) miscellaneous, 3%. These percentages were estimated from Hunter's graphs. In 1947, Hunter published two surveys, one using replies from 665 schools and obtained in 1940 and the second utilizing data from 408 schools gathered in 1947. In these studies the statements of objectives were placed in rank order in terms of frequency of teacher response; only the higher ranking objectives are listed here.

Objectives	1940 Rank (665 schools)	1947 Rank (408 schools)
Scientific method	3	1
Worthwhile ideals and habits	4	2
Understanding the environment	2	3
Understanding personal health needs	1	4
Knowledge of the environment	6	5
Develop the power of observation	5	6
Withhold conclusions until facts secured	10	7
Information useful in solving life problems	11	8
Appreciation of the environment	9	9
Attitude free from dogma and superstition	7	10
Evaluate and interpret data	8	11

Hunter noted a growing emphasis upon the methodology of science as an objective for high school science teaching. These studies show a changing emphasis in the teaching of secondary school science and in turn reveal the objectives subscribed to by the high school teacher.

Noll (1939) examined 130 sets of science objectives from various sources, (committee reports, articles in periodicals, textbooks in science education, state and national agencies) and compiled a common list ranked in terms of percentage of mention. His results were: 1) knowledge of the principles and applications of science, 34.7%; 2) interest in science, 7.9%; 3) appreciation of the beauties of nature, and of the commonplace, 6.9%; 4) appreciation of the work of scientists, 6.9%; 5) ability to use the scientific method, 6.9%; 6) knowledge leading to an understanding of the nature and organization of the environment, 6.4%; 7) preparation for further work in science and for college entrance, 6.4%; 8) desirable habits of work and study, 6.4%; 9) ability to do useful tasks, 5.4%; 10) scientific attitude, 4.9%; 11) exploration to acquaint the pupil with science and to help him to orient himself with respect to the different sciences, 4.0%; 12) habits of healthful living, 1.5%. Noll found the greatest emphasis to be upon knowledge aims (51.5%), with appreciations (13.8%) and abilities (12.3%) ranking second and third in importance. Reusser (1923) obtained replies from 212 high schools on the aims of biology teaching. He found the "most common aims" to be: 1) to broaden the pupil's knowledge of his own body through the study of plants and animals; and 2) to make good citizens through a knowledge of good food, health and living conditions. "Less important aims" for biology teaching were: 1) accurate observations; 2) to think clearly and form logical conclusions based on facts; and 3) develop an interest in life and environment. He also found that 70% of the teachers considered human biology the most important division of the course.

Hurd (1949) analyzed nine of the most widely used high school textbooks of biology published between 1938 and 1948 for the authors' statements of objectives. Those most frequently mentioned were:

1. To aid students to work with problems that are real to them. (8)
2. To develop competence in the use of the scientific method of thinking. (7)
3. To develop a functional understanding of the principles and generalizations of biology. (7)
4. To develop, through understanding, a desire to use the scientific attitudes toward the solution of problems. (6)
5. To help students develop the intellectual competence and proper attitudes that are essential to their adjustment to the world about them. (6)
6. To develop an understanding and the attitudes which will lead to constructive action on social and economic problems of wide concern. (6)
7. To aid students in the development of worthy leisure time activities. (5)
8. To acquaint students with vocational possibilities in the biological fields. (4)
9. To instill in students a recognition of science as a way of seeking knowledge rather than as a set of facts or an organization of knowledge. (3)

McKibben (1947) analyzed 150 sources for statements of general education biology objectives to determine any changes in thinking that may have taken place in a twenty-year period. She compared statements published from 1926 to 1935 with those reported in the period 1936–1945. She then determined a relative ranking of the objectives for the two periods:

Objectives	1926–35	1936–45
A. Intellectual objectives:		
1. A study of biology should develop in the pupil a proficiency in the use of the scientific method.	14%	10%
2. The study of biology should create certain desirable scientific attitudes in the pupil.	7%	7%
3. The study of biology should equip the pupil with the knowledge of biological facts and principles.	24%	20%
4. The study of biology should increase the pupil's interest in living things.	5%	7%
B. Practical objectives:		
5. The study of biology should enable the pupil to make the proper social adjustments.	4%	7%
6. The study of biology should have certain economic value for the pupil.	9%	13%
7. The study of biology should enable the pupils to make wise vocational selections.	2%	4%
8. The study of biology should help a pupil make better use of leisure time.	3%	5%
9. The biology course should prepare a pupil for further study toward a career.	4%	3%
10. The study of biology should direct a pupil to more healthful living.	9%	8%
11. The study of biology should make life more enjoyable and more meaningful.	5%	4%
12. The study of biology should develop a more ethical character.	3%	0%
13. General applications.	8%	10%
14. Miscellaneous applications.	2%	2%

Brandwein, Watson, and Blackwood (1958) studied the trend in expected outcomes from high school biology teaching from an analysis of the "10 best-selling textbooks in 1935 and in 1955; also from a study of curriculums in 72 varied school systems, small and large, rural and urban." They found that the trend in teaching biology was "toward dealing with the concepts of biology which will help students to understand themselves as organisms and their environments in terms of the interrelationship of the organism and the environment." They further pointed out that in a modern biology course all students might gain:

> "1. A sufficient understanding of the concepts of biology to enable those who will not become doctors, nurses, veterinarians, farmers, or other agents of public health or biological production to cooperate intelligently with those who are.
>
> 2. The opportunities for a practical understanding of the method of the biologist which will give them the confidence, in consultation with experts, to attempt the solution of problems which they have to face in their individual and social lives.
>
> 3. The incentive to become biologists (scientists with special interest in biology) or experts in applying the concepts of biology (e.g., doctors, nurses)."

Summary

The purposes for the teaching of biology which are accepted by the classroom teacher and which in turn guide the writing of textbooks are more likely to describe the actual directions of biology teaching than those postulated by national curriculum committees. However, in both instances there are likely to be discrepancies between the teacher's stated objectives and class and laboratory practices. Although teaching of the "scientific method" typically ranks first as an objective of biology teaching, teaching practices that might accomplish this goal are seldom found. Textbooks frequently contain an introductory chapter describing the methods of biology but afterwards little reference is made to the topic. Studies on testing and evaluation fail to show that growth in the ability "to solve problems scientifically" receives serious consideration when teachers judge student achievement. On the other hand, to assume that the objectives of science teaching can be achieved from unstructured teaching as a concomitant result of learning the facts of the science does not seem to be supported by psychological research or the intuitive judgment of research scientists.

Both the investigations and committee reports on objectives illustrate changes in emphasis and the emergence of new objectives for biology teaching. This should be expected if the characteristics of a liberal education are to be closely related to changing cultural patterns. The recent criticisms of science teaching in the high school have been in the nature of disagreement with the current objectives and their inconsistency with the educational demands of contemporary society. The national curriculum studies now in progress have proposed new directions for the teaching of high school biology, directions which place more emphasis upon the processes of science.

XI

Investigations of Criteria for the Selection of Course Content

CENTRAL TO CURRICULUM DEVELOPMENT is the determination of appropriate course content. The accelerated increase in available knowledge makes the selecting of the significant knowledge from a discipline for a high school course of 160–180 hours' duration a greater problem than ever. In addition, the selection must be comprehensible to non-college bound students, the majority, with further consideration for the student who can profit from advanced training.

There are several approaches to the development of course content in biology: 1) the use of "objective" procedures to isolate the knowledge according to an assumed criteria (for example, frequency of biological items in the public press); 2) the establishment of certain philosophical assumptions which may serve as a unifying theme (meeting the personal-social needs of young people); 3) importance in understanding the discipline (using the opinions of leading scientists); or 4) a combination of these approaches.

Hurd (1954) found that a major concern of high school science teachers was the question of what to teach. An examination of 1,373 articles on the teaching of science published during the fifty years prior to 1951 showed that the majority of teachers used the following criteria to select the content for their science courses: the knowledge is interesting to the majority of students; it is practical; it is related to everyday living; it has reference to the local community and has wide social and economic significance.

Several investigators sought to determine significant course content through an analysis of biological items appearing in newspapers and widely read magazines. The assumption underlying these investigations was that the study of biology should enable the student to read intelligently those publications he would normally read throughout his lifetime. Finley and Caldwell (1923) analyzed 13,796 pages of newspapers, representing issues from 11 prominent newspapers, for biological content. They found 3,061 articles on biology distributed according to the following categories: 1) health, 897; 2) animals, 755; 3) plants, 660; 4) food, 533; 5) organization of producers, 81; 6) nature, 74; 7) evolution, 47; 8) fictitious, 14. The articles first in frequency were also first in the quantity of material.

Curtis (1924) examined a total of 5,566 articles appearing in the public press and found that only 13.7% required no scientific background for understanding. A total of 962 scientific terms were found in the articles of which less than two percent were defined in the news items. Curtis concluded that courses in general science need to devote more space to the biological sciences based upon the frequency of biological articles and biological vocabulary in the public press.

Searle and Ruch (1926) studied a sample of the science articles in a number of magazines covering a ten-year period. Representative magazines used in the investigation were *Science, Scientific Monthly, Saturday Evening Post, The Atlantic Monthly, The Literary Digest, The American* and others. They found that 62.2% of the science articles were about biology plus an additional 2.4% on agriculture. The highest ranking articles by biological topics were: 1) man, 17.1%; 2) mammals, 10.5%; 3) health, 9.2%; 4) insects, 8.2%; 5) disease, 7.2%; 6) food, 6.7%; 7) respiration, 5.0%.

Hill (1930) investigated the content of 591 issues of non-specialized magazines, including *The American, The Atlantic, Harpers, Scribners,* and *The Saturday Evening Post,* for the amount of space devoted to science. He found that the most commonly discussed biological topics in terms of the percent of space devoted to them, and which could be easily read by students who had had the Kansas biology course, were: 1) animal biology, 52.4%; 2) human biology, 28.6% (mostly on health);

3) plant biology, 6.0%; and 4) general biology, 2.69%. Eleven percent of the articles were considered too difficult to understand for a student who had completed the Kansas biology course.

Merrill (1929) sought an objective procedure to develop the content of a high school botany course to meet social needs as they appear in human activities. He analyzed and compared the space devoted to articles on botany in popular periodical magazines with the percent of space devoted to the same topic in botany textbooks. Among his findings were these: 1) *textbooks* devote three times more space to lower forms of plants, twice as much space to descriptions of plants, seven times more space to plant structure, and three times more space to the function of parts; 2) *periodicals* devote seven times more space to food producing plants, ten times as much space to plant culture, five times as much space to the control of plant diseases and twice as much space to conservation.

Novak (1942) analyzed 1,461 issues of the *New York Times* and found that of 15 major science topics appearing in this newspaper, 6 were biological in nature; namely: health and medicine; animal life; man and behavior; gardening and agriculture; conservation, and plant life. Of the total science articles in the 75,000 newspaper pages examined, 50.5% of the space was devoted to biology. DeLoach (1941) studied a year's issue of *Life* magazine and found that of 56 science articles 41 dealt with the biological sciences. Medicine accounted for 17 articles and zoology was next in frequency with 10 articles.

Another approach to the selection of course content has been to determine the common misconceptions and superstitions of young people about biological topics and assume that a proper course of instruction in biology should incorporate content appropriate to changing these erroneous beliefs. Vinal (1922) studied the mistaken ideas of young people in 14 different classes ranging from junior high school through college. He found that "old sayings" which are untrue and acquired in the early grades are long remembered. Vinal concluded that students depend more on hearsay about biological topics than on observation or thinking and that biological ignorance was widespread.

Maller and Lundeen (1933) investigated the sources of superstitious beliefs and factors that contribute toward the learning and unlearning of unfounded ideas. They found that most superstitious beliefs came from friends. The second greatest influence was the home. Third, were such sources as books, newspapers, school and church. Direct observation was found to contribute least to the development of superstitious beliefs and was also the best way for correcting them. Students who preferred to read books on science and invention showed fewer superstitions than those preferring books of fiction, adventure, and mystery.

Salt (1936) investigated the prevalence of health misconceptions and superstitions possessed by students at several grade levels and in relation to their sex, race, socio-economic status and geographical location. He found pupils in the lower grades had more health misconceptions than pupils in the upper grades, and that negro students had more misconceptions than white students of the same grade. Socio-economic status of the student had little relationship to the number of their misconceptions about health.

Caldwell and Lundeen (1939) in a series of studies on unfounded beliefs concluded that: 1) specific instruction can change unfounded ideas as most of them seem to be due to a lack of correct information; 2) unfounded ideas are wide-spread; and 3) education and experience tend to reduce the number of superstitions among students.

Textbooks and courses of study, since they represent the considered judgment of one or more persons presumably experienced in teaching biology, have been the subject of analysis and synthesis to develop "better" biology courses. Meier (1927) analyzed a number of high school textbooks in biology and found that nearly 50% of the content consisted of health materials. The more common topics "included the structure, functions, and hygiene of the human body, the relations of plants and animals to human welfare, particularly with reference to food and disease and problems pertaining to public health."

Chappelear (1929) investigated the amount of health content in: 1) five high school textbooks of biology; 2) 10 recent courses of study in biology; 3) 13 sets of College Entrance Board questions; and 4) 20 sets of New York State Regent questions in biology. He then secured answers from 50 teachers of biology as to the amount of time they devoted to various health topics. He found that: 1) the content of biology textbooks varied between 33% and 40% on health materials; 2) 38.8% of the content of biology syllabi was on health; 3) 32.2% of the questions on the biology college entrance examinations were on health; and 4) on the Regent Examinations in biology, 31.9% of the questions were on health. Chappelear pointed out that, based upon his analysis, a typical biology course of 36 weeks' duration would have 13 weeks devoted to the study of health. He noted a considerable overlapping between the health content of general science and biology textbooks. Furthermore, that many teachers not only utilized the health topics of the textbooks and courses of study but selected additional health material for their biology courses.

Webb and Vinal (1934) analyzed the content of 13 courses of study in biology, none of which were over three years old. They found that great emphasis was given to the social and economic aspects of biology; however, 11 of the 13 courses of study did touch upon heredity, environment and evolution. The major topics of biology usually considered: 1) classification of living things; 2) cells—cell structure and protoplasm; 3) lower plant life; 4) the living plant—structure and function of major parts; 5) plant ecology; 6) forestry—conservation practices; 7) animals—structures and functions and from simple to complex forms with an emphasis upon insects; 8) the human body—structure and functions with related hygiene; 9) food—organized around a balanced diet; 10) alcohol, narcotics and food adulteration; 11) interrelationship of organisms; 12) heredity, environment and evolution; and 13) miscellaneous topics (biographies, scientific progress). In four courses of study the "behavior of living things" was considered, three mentioned the "methods of science" and one the "value of studying biology."

Caldwell and Weller (1932) obtained the opinions of 30 college biologists about the factual and topical content found in 11 of the most widely used high school biology textbooks. Each of the 30 college biologists checked the topics he felt should be included in a high school course and was also asked to comment on his selection of topics and his omissions, and to suggest additional topics. Between two-thirds and three-fourths of the college biologists would *increase* the emphasis upon the following subdivisions of biology: ecology, taxonomy, morphology, genetics, embryology, anatomy and physiology. It was felt that the classification of plants and animals should receive slightly less attention, even though the textbooks already devoted little space to the topic. Four-fifths of the biologists would include a brief study of elements, compounds, energy, physical and chemical change in the biology course. Human behavior and mental hygiene were rated low although most of the judges would include the topics. Few would either omit man or make man the leading feature of the course, but almost all would include care of the human structures, public health, and the study of foods. Strongly recommended by the biologists was a consideration of geographic distribution of plants and animals, their economic value, insect pest control, conservation of wild life and biographies of a dozen or so biologists. While 90% of the texts contained material on alcohol, tobacco and drugs, less than two-thirds of the judges would include these topics and then only with minor emphasis. The college biologists felt that heredity and environment should be included in high school biology but would not give much space to the topic and recommended only scant attention to the theories of evolution.

The authors of *A Program for Teaching Science,* Thirty-first Yearbook, Part I, National Society for the Study of Education (1932) recommended that course content should be selected in terms of the significant principles of science "that ramify most widely into human affairs." This recommendation was an effort to direct science teaching toward the larger ideas of science expressed as principles or generalizations, and away from an inventory of discrete facts. The research on retention of learning provided considerable justification for focusing course content on the principles of biology.

The "principles" concept stimulated many research studies during the next twenty-five years in an effort to identify the more significant biological principles around which to build the high school biology course. Various techniques were used to attack the problem. The usual procedure was first to establish educational criteria for selecting the principles from authoritative biological literature. Competent research biologists were then asked to rate or rank the principles for their importance in the discipline and to verify the accuracy of statement. The principles were then organized according to their importance for general education, suitability for a grade level, or their teachability.

Among the studies on the identification of principles of biology were: Menzies (1927), Bently (1934), Moyer (1936), Olds (1936), Weid (1940), Martin (1945), Blanchet (1946), Washton (1951), McKibben (1955), Friborough (1957), and Rabb (1960). Other studies which have identified principles useful in planning biology curricula are: Bergman (1947), entomology; Irish (1949), soil conservation; Glidden (1956), conservation; Mallinson (1949), consumer science; Leonelli (1947), O'Connor (1950), and Smith (1951), general science. Studies of a similar nature have been carried out in the physical sciences and for elementary science. The number of biological principles identified in these studies run into the hundreds, the following are representative:

1. "Reproduction is a fundamental biological process that provides for the continuance of life on the earth by providing new individuals." (McKibben)
2. "All living organisms (except viruses and bacteriophage) carry on the common life processes; reproduction, growth, nutrition, excretion, respiration, and irritability." (Martin)
3. "Since plants alone have the power to use solar energy for

the manufacture of food materials, all other living things depend on the green plant." (Menzies)

Curriculum workers have felt that a useful approach to the selection of course content in biology was to use the judgment of experienced high school teachers. LeMaster (1952) compared the subject matter of 12 city and state courses of study in biology with the content recommended by 36 successful high school biology teachers. He found agreement on the following topics: 1) classification of plants and animals; 2) genetics; 3) ecology; 4) reproduction; 5) obtaining and using food; 6) structure and organization of living things; 7) conservation. The teachers would place a greater emphasis on: 1) behavioral reactions; 2) modern control of disease; 3) biology and atomic energy; and 4) biology of flight. They would place less emphasis on paleontology than outlined in the courses of study. Tyrell (1958) obtained 931 replies from biology teachers who were members of the *National Association of Biology Teachers* as to the *one area* of instruction they felt was the most important for high school students. The following topics were judged to be the most significant: 1) biological principles; 2) conservation and natural resources; 3) essential life processes; and 4) human physiology. A. W. Hurd (1934) obtained opinions from members of the *National Association for Research in Science Teaching,* the *Central Association of Science and Mathematics Teachers,* and from 50 teachers in colleges, universities and departments of education regarding criteria for developing high school science courses. The most frequently listed criteria were those which: 1) explain scientific attitudes and show their effect on man's thinking; 2) explain the methods of science; 3) appeal to the immediate interests and sustain pupil interests; 4) encourage the belief in, and practice of, desirable social ideals involving science; 5) are of direct use to pupils in their everyday living; 6) explain the local environment; 7) are within the capacities of the pupils; 8) make a direct and immediate contribution to the welfare of the social order; 9) stimulate the discussion of science problems found in the news of the day; and 10) provide unity and coherence to biology as a science.

A procedure for selecting the content of courses has been the use of "expert" advice from a "qualified" committee of high school teachers, research biologists, and educators. The proportional representation from each group has varied but has rarely been equal. The reports outlined in the earlier chapters of this study illustrate the product of these committees.

More than other high school science courses the content of biology courses has been subject to influence by special interest groups. There is no real way to judge the extent of this influence except to note the content of high school biology textbooks and curricula for omissions and inclusions which the research biologist could only view with suspicion. Topics which for one reason or another (political, social custom, religious) have been minimized or maximized in the curriculum to a greater extent than biologists would support are: evolution; narcotics and tobacco; health topics and practices; conservation; eugenics and sex instruction. Limitations on the use of living organisms in high school biology have restricted the best biology teaching in several cities. Even the professional biologist has at times brought about an imbalance in the curriculum through efforts to maximize his field in the curriculum. The growing body of biological knowledge and the changing emphasis among the diverse fields, make the choice of content for a high school course an increasing problem.

Traditions and fashions, both in biology and education, are reflected in the secondary school biology curriculum. The educator wants the biology content to be useful for *all* students; the biologist emphasizes the content useful to biologists. New theories and discoveries in biology enter the curriculum only after a considerable time lag and then seldom replace any topics.

The degree to which research studies and committee reports influence the high school biology curriculum is a matter of debate. It would perhaps be accurate to state that they determine the curriculum to the extent they influence the authors of biology textbooks. Martin's (1952) survey showed that over 90% of the biology teachers used a single textbook; the textbook then becomes the criterion for the selection of course content.

Tests such as the Regents' Examinations, College Entrance Board Examinations and other standardized biology tests influence what is taught in schools. Since many of these tests provide evidence on only one facet of biological education, the student's inventory of facts and names, teaching is focused in this direction. An understanding of the science of biology is minimized because it is not or cannot be evaluated.

Another approach to curriculum development in biology is to consider the interests and preferences of pupils. Washton (1941) found that New York City Students who had taken high school biology were most interested in man, heredity and evolution. Blanc (1958) in a similar study in the Denver schools found heredity, evolution, nervous system and control of the body, disease, reproduction, circulation, alcohol and drugs, balance of nature, economic importance of mammals to man, and the structure of mammals to be of major importance. Among the topics of low interest to students were: structure and function of plants and animals (exclusive of man), and classification. Pupils graded "A" and "D" did not differ greatly in their interest patterns except that "A" students were more inclined to be interested in topics that were emphasized in the textbook.

Relyea (1937) studied the biological interests of high school sophomore girls before they took biology and found them to be identified with pets, gardens, flowers, and the familiar plants and animals. Zim (1942), using several techniques, investigated the interests of adolescents in biology. He found that 55% of the girls' and 43% of the boys' interests in science could be identified with biological topics. Zim concludes that: "adolescents are interested in living things around them; biological interests are specific and most frequently related to health, disease, physiology, anatomy and animal life; and the interests of boys and girls in biology are different."

Curtis (1924) found that the interests of pupils and adults

in cities and good-sized towns were more in the physical sciences than in the biological and that girls and women were more interested in biology than boys and men. The topics of greatest biological interest to adults were: animals, flowers, evolution, plants, diet, gardening, snakes, trees, birds and physiology. The biological interests of children were: animals, flowers, plants, fish, snakes, trees, birds, and "germs."

Henderson (1957) studied the interests of pupils related to human physiology and found that they were of a "practical nature", but differed from those thought to be most worthwhile by physicians. Bunce (1952) had high school graduates who did not enter college evaluate their high school science courses. In general more men than women thought they were of value and both felt there was a need to make science courses more practical for everyday living.

Fitzpatrick (1937) questioned the reliability of student interest studies and the development of subject content from them. Klise and Oliver (1947) found that the popularity of topics as judged by students varied with different teachers.

These and similar studies in biological education appear to indicate that young people are primarily interested in those phases of biology directly and specifically related to man and his well-being and other topics of a "practical nature."

Summary

The diversity of fields in biology has posed many problems for the selection of content suitable for a high school course in biology. Some curriculum makers have sought to make the course "practical" and "useful" and have, therefore, explored the interests of students and the biological knowledge valuable in daily living. The professional biologists have made use of different assumptions for determining course content. Disagreements on the purposes of the secondary school and the function of science in a liberal education leave the matter of course content in biology with many unanswered questions.

Most of the curriculum investigators have sought a way for

determining the content of courses by a criterion that would define a specific body of significant knowledge. It seems apparent that such procedures are futile in terms of the rapid increase of biological knowledge since mid-century. There is need for a clear statement of philosophical assumptions to guide the development of new biology curriculums. These should indicate the contribution of biology to a liberal education and the development of a scientific literacy on the part of the typical high school student.

XII

Investigations on Biology Textbooks

THE BIOLOGY TEXTBOOK in the American school represents not only the content but also the organization for the majority of biology courses. There is little question that it strongly influences the instructional, learning and testing procedures of the course. Whatever is new in curriculum theory and content reaches the majority of teachers and the students by way of textbooks. Although frequently criticized, they nevertheless have been the major guide to whatever is "good" in courses. Much of the "bad" in science teaching has developed from the improper use of textbooks, for example, the fetish that they must be "covered" in nine months, or the teacher who feels they represent all that is important to know in a subject.

Research on textbooks in science is limited. Few studies have been made on their use as a teaching device. Analyses of the content of textbooks are common and are used to determine the "real" curriculum in science courses.

Richards (1923) analyzed the content of six of the most widely used high school biology texts. He used a word count to indicate the relative emphasis given to each topic and developed a synthesis to represent "an average biology textbook." The results of his study are shown in the table on the following page.

Welzin (1933) analyzed five popular textbooks in high school biology and found little agreement among them as to content or organization. He noted that not one reference for supplementary reading was common to all five texts and that Darwin, Edwards, Lazear and Pasteur were the only biologists mentioned in each of the five textbooks.

Presson (1930) analyzed the contents of the seven most widely used textbooks in high school biology and determined the percentage of total space devoted to each topic.

195

The "Average Biology Course" (Richards, 1923)

Rank Topic	1000's of words
1. Vertebrates	68.0
2. Insects	51.8
3. Lower plants	51.2
4. Public Health	47.1
5. Foods and dietetics; alcohol and drugs	39.8
6. Health and Disease	30.1
7. Seeds	26.5
8. Respiration and excretion	25.6
9. Classification	24.0
10. Nervous system and sense organs	22.9
11. Stems	22.6
12. Metazoa	21.2
13. Molluscs	21.2
14. Plants and Human Welfare	20.8
15. Flowers and Work	20.8
16. Blood and Circulation	20.5
17. Digestion and absorption	19.5
18. Environment	18.9
19. Roots	17.8
20. Structure and function of living things	15.6
21. Interrelations of plants and animals	14.8
22. Crayfish	14.8
23. Worms	13.9
24. Leaves	13.5
25. Forests and protection of	12.5
26. Evolution	12.2
27. Protozoa	10.0
28. Great men and history	9.6
29. Growth, development, sex	8.5
30. Why study biology	6.1
31. Parasitism	5.7
32. Fruits	4.9
33. Man in general	4.5
34. Higher mental processes	3.6
35. Human machine	3.5

Space Analysis of Seven Biology Textbooks (Presson, 1930)

Topic	Percentage of Space
Plant biology	*30.6*
Cells	1.6
Seeds	2.6
Roots	1.5
Stems	1.9
Forestry	2.5
Leaves	2.5
Plant physiology	3.7
Flowers	2.9
Fruits	1.2
Plant breeding	1.1
Bacteria	1.9
Lower forms of plants	1.5
Soil	1.2
Economics of plants	1.8
Classification of plants	.8
Conservation of plants	1.0
Symbiosis	1.0
Animal biology	*29.7*
Insects	7.0
Crustaceans	1.5
Worms	.8
Molluscs	.4
Protozoa	1.3
Simple metazoa	.7
Amphibians	2.3
Fishes	2.2
Reptiles	.6
Birds	3.7
Mammals	2.5
Classification of animals	.9
Animal breeding	.7
Life processes	3.0
Economics of invertebrates	1.5
Economics of vertebrates	.8
Human biology	*32.9*
Structure	2.2
Foods	5.9
Digestion	2.9
Respiration	2.4
Circulation	3.1
Nervous system	4.3
Excretion	1.1
Health	9.1
Stimulants, narcotics, and drugs	1.9
Miscellaneous	*6.8*
Introductory material	3.7
Heredity and evolution	2.6
Biography	.6

Christy (1936) analyzed 17 textbooks of high school biology, published between 1906–1936, to determine the percent of space devoted to the different phases of subject matter. He found, for example, that taxonomy and morphology receive less emphasis in more recent textbooks compared with those published before 1910. The degree to which particular topics were stressed varied with the author as well as with the time of publication; however, the diversity in emphasis was the most typical characteristic of the texts.

Percentage of Space Devoted to the Different Phases of
Biology Textual Material (from Christy)

*Author	Year Published	Taxonomy	Morphology	Natural History	Ecology	Health	Heredity	Appreciation	Prac. Applications	Miscellaneous	Physiology
Hunter	1907	16.37	39.99	8.67	9.32	9.05	0.05	1.49	4.62	3.96	6.27
Bailey & C	1908	11.79	39.36	9.50	4.74	8.85	0.55	0.26	5.96	2.67	16.28
Peabody & H	1912	6.90	23.16	6.54	1.29	19.25	1.57	7.09	17.32	2.54	11.08
Hunter	1914	5.33	10.37	2.00	6.29	25.99	4.52	8.76	12.39	3.12	21.16
Hodge & D	1918	12.95	2.23	12.93	0.89	13.26	4.68	14.16	35.98	2.42	0.21
Moon	1926	6.01	27.40	13.28	2.53	13.78	1.76	6.97	9.89	3.71	14.65
Atwood	1922	5.58	22.81	12.58	6.77	8.86	9.76	2.71	16.90	4.85	9.12
Clement	1924	4.73	12.33	8.47	3.74	20.34	3.28	5.12	10.19	4.62	27.13
Gruenberg	1925	6.14	13.59	3.98	4.42	29.00	7.08	6.11	12.91	7.54	13.48
Atwood	1927	9.04	19.91	9.65	7.63	9.14	6.60	9.76	18.84	2.11	7.15
Meier & Meier	1931	11.46	23.29	11.25	4.00	12.16	3.08	8.37	16.08	1.30	8.92
Pieper, B & F	1932	5.94	14.93	13.06	15.15	10.58	3.68	5.46	14.93	5.61	15.96
Wheat	1932	3.63	11.48	9.92	10.72	5.30	11.74	13.44	14.38	4.64	14.80
Kinsey	1933	7.45	8.23	14.40	19.91	8.66	7.86	12.76	9.83	6.43	5.13
Baker & M	1933	4.67	3.73	20.46	9.23	11.20	7.27	16.28	7.11	2.97	6.93
Mank	1933	6.73	14.30	8.33	9.20	13.94	4.47	7.68	13.23	4.58	17.69
Fitzpatrick & H	1935	5.82	11.79	11.89	10.16	7.23	7.79	8.11	9.66	4.06	17.75

* The textbooks given in the table by the author's name are:
Hunter, G.W. 1907. *Elements of Botany.*
Bailey, L.H., and W.M. Coleman. 1908. *First Course in Biology.*
Peabody, J.E., and A.E. Hunt. 1913. *Elementary Biology.*
Hunter, G.W. 1914. *A Civic Biology.*
Hodge, C.F. and J. Dawson. 1918. *Civic Biology.*
Moon, J.T. 1921. *Biology for Beginners.*
Atwood, W.H. 1922. *Civic and Economic Biology.*
Clement, A.G. 1924. *Living Things.*
Gruenberg, B.C. 1925. *Biology and Human Life.*
Atwood, W.H. 1927. *Biology.*
Meier, W.H.D., and L. Meier. 1931. *Essentials of Biology.*
Pieper, C.J., W.L. Beauchamp, and O.D. Frank. 1932. *Everyday Problems in Biology.*
Wheat, F.M., and E.T. Fitzpatrick. 1932. *General Biology.*
Kinsey, A. 1933. *New Introduction to Biology.*
Mank, H.G. 1933. *The Living World.*
Fitzpatrick, F.L., and R.E. Horton. 1936. *Biology.*

Blanc (1957) analyzed ten high school biology textbooks published since 1951 to determine the major emphasis given to the various content areas and topics. The *areas* emphasized the most were:

1. conservation and natural resources
2. study of the human body
3. study of flowering plants
4. genetics and eugenics

The individual *topics* receiving the most emphasis were:

Rank	Topic
1	structure and function of leaves
1	foods and nutrition
1	process of digestion
1	principles of heredity
5	physical factors of the environment
5	inheritance in man
5	evidence of change in evolution
5	conservation of forests
9	sense organs and sensations
9	soil and water conservation
9	conservation of wildlife

Rosen (1959) in his study on the origins of high school general biology, notes that the course "marks the first successful revolt by high school science teachers against the domination of biology course content and methods by college professors." After tracing the development of the biology course in high school Rosen concludes that: "By 1936, it appeared that in biology, at least, a panacea for the ills of high school science teaching has been found." Fifty years earlier Dawson (1909) observed: "The biology, or rather the botany and zoology of our high schools has been from the first undifferentiated from the work of the college. The high school textbooks contain the most modern biological thought and theory that is advanced in our universities . . . They are so complete that they form compendiums from which I have seen graduate students studying preparatory to taking an examination for the degree of Doctor of Philosophy. The books announced that they had been prepared for high school texts."

Mallinson, Sturm and Mallinson (1950), using the *Flesch* formula, investigated the reading difficulty of 26 textbooks in high school biology. They found that eleven rated eighth grade or below in difficulty, twelve rated eighth to ninth grade, and three ninth grade completed or tenth grade. One of the textbooks had a sixth grade completed reading level and another extended well into a college reading level. Kessler (1941) studied the readability of 35 books on biological subjects published between 1931–1939 intended for reading by high school students. He found that 21 out of the 35 books were suitable for tenth-grade biology students. Major (1955) investigated, using the *Flesch* formula, the readability of ten commonly used college general biology textbooks and the effects of readability elements on comprehension. He concluded that the complaint of college students about the great extent of technical terms was apparently justified.

Pressey (1924) analyzed the technical vocabulary found in high school biology textbooks. She found an average of 1,393 technical terms of which 675 could be classified as "essential vocabulary" and 677 as "accessory vocabulary" and 41 as "not necessary." Texts in the other high school sciences had the following vocabulary counts: general science, 1,564; chemistry, 1,297; physics, 1,040; geography, 1,132; and physiology, 866. There were only 215 words that could be classified as a "common science list." She concluded that the object of most science textbooks "seems to be to include the greatest possible assortment of facts." Powers (1925) found that the number of uncommon words in four high school biology textbooks were, respectively, 2,152, 2,270, 2,037, and 1,759. Between 50 and 60% of the uncommon words were used but once in the text and 15% were used only twice. The Thorndike Teachers Word List was used as the criterion for "commonness."

Powers (1926) compared the list of uncommon words found in high school science textbooks with the vocabulary in 50 magazine articles on scientific subjects, and three popular scientific books. He concluded that: the "authors of textbooks are using in their books many words children will never see again after they have finished the required class work."

Cretzinger (1941) studied 54 biology textbooks published in the period 1800–1933 and found that new biological theories and concepts move slowly into secondary school textbooks. Commenting upon the teaching of evolution, Cretzinger observed that: "There was no law to prevent the teaching of evolution in any state until 1925, when Tennessee took the first legal stand against it," yet little space had been given to the topic in high school biology textbooks.

Crowell (1937) analyzed 13 high school biology textbooks for their treatment of the important skills and attitudes related to the methods of science. He found that while authors recognized the need for students to understand scientific inquiry, the average textbook writer treated the topic poorly and inadequately. Lampkin (1949) analyzed 12 high school textbooks, three each in biology, general science, chemistry and physics, for materials descriptive or explanatory of scientific inquiry. Twelve adult readers of "high intelligence" read the textbook material to identify the passages related to certain aspects of scientific inquiry. In general the readers were not able to recognize the material on scientific inquiry. Christy (1936) found that biology textbooks and courses of study widely used in the period 1930–1934 gave the "scientific attitude aim" first priority in the list of objectives for teaching biology.

Finley (1926) examined the organization of the 17 textbooks of biology in use in 1926. He found that eleven were organized around the separate biological sciences, botany, zoology, and physiology. Six of the biology texts were of the "blended," "synthetic," or "general type," illustrating an effort to present biology as a science of living things. Christy (1936) analyzed 32 high school biology textbooks and found 13 were of the tripartite arrangement and 19 of the "united organization." No new books with the tripartite arrangement were published between 1929 and 1936. He found that several of the more recent biology texts were organized "around important problems which involve experiments, among other things, in their solution." Martin (1952) in a survey of 736 high schools found that in 499 schools the biology textbook represented the way the course was organized for instructional purposes.

Martin (1952) found in a sample of 786 high schools which offered biology that 93.6% of the schools reported the use of a single basic textbook, while 6.4% reported using several texts along with magazines, industry-prepared materials, and supplementary references of various types to formulate the course. In 264, or 33.4% of the schools, the basic biology text was selected from a State-approved list. In 771 out of 786 schools the teacher was in some way involved in selecting the textbooks, but apparently in no case was this an exclusive prerogative of the teacher but required at some point the approval of other persons. Barnes (1959) found that only 5.4% of all the teachers of science were dissatisfied with the textbook they were using, but when teachers of only the larger schools were considered the number rose to 11.9%. St. Lawrence (1951) found that 59.4% of 170 biology teachers interviewed disliked the text they were using, 26.5% were noncommittal and 14.1% liked the text.

St. Lawrence (1951) surveyed the teaching aids found in high school biology textbooks and then investigated the extent to which teachers made use of them. The aids commonly found were: 1) references; 2) projects; 3) problems; 4) suggested reports; 5) tests; 6) demonstrations; 7) vocabulary lists; 8) suggested field trips; 9) experiments; 10) a listing of biological principles; 11) sources of visual aids; 12) outlines of summaries; 13) review questions at the end of a chapter; and 14) guide questions at the beginning of the chapter. St. Lawrence interviewed 170 biology teachers regarding their use of these teaching aids and found that only three, vocabulary lists, review questions and outlines or summaries, were commonly used by as many as fifty percent of the teachers. A second study showed that teachers preferred to use their own reference lists and wanted students to develop their own projects; older experienced teachers employed fewer of the teaching aids than younger teachers; and teachers in the larger high schools used the textbook aids as frequently as teachers in smaller schools.

Stiles (1924) analyzed the illustrative materials found in ten widely used high school biology textbooks to determine the quality and quantity of illustrative material. He found that about 70% of the illustrations in these books could be considered good but that there was a wide variation. Most of the poor pictures either were too small and did not show detail or failed to draw the attention of the onlooker to the parts the author wished to stress. The percent of space in biology textbooks devoted to pictures ranged from 7.1 to 50.3 with an average of 22.8%. Neal (1940) analyzed eight biology textbooks published between 1934–1940 and found that 23.6% of the total space in the texts was devoted to pictures. He also noted a trend toward a greater use of representative drawings and away from analytical drawings.

Burdick (1960) studied the value of cross-section and perspective-cutaway drawings in high school science textbooks in terms of the contribution they make to reading comprehension contrasted to identical passages of text material without drawings. He found that the drawings make no measurable contribution to the student's reading comprehension in studying texts.

Summary

There is little in the research studies on biology textbooks to suggest better ways of preparing a textbook. Their authoritarian nature has been a subject of criticism but changes needed to make them less so are seldom mentioned. The basic function of a textbook in a science course is not clear. Is it a learning guide or a summary of useful knowledge determined by some criterion? The text versions of the AIBS Biological Sciences Curriculum Study have each been organized around a central theme to provide a stronger continuity and integration of subject content than is typically found in the majority of textbooks.

The science textbook as a learning resource is one of the unexplored areas of educational research.

XIII

The Learning of Biology

A MEASURE of successful teaching is the extent to which the students achieve the expectations defined by the objectives of the course. Lessons are structured and teaching techniques are used that give promise of obtaining the stated goal. If it is to learn the parts of an earthworm or flower in order to duplicate these on a test, there are ways to teach that will effect this result. On the other hand to develop an understanding of the "inter-relations of all creatures" or a concept of science as an "intellectual activity" requires quite different teaching procedures. An inability to relate course objectives to principles of learning and to teaching techniques has been a major cause of failure in the attempts to improve education in the sciences.

A few studies have been made to determine just what a student does remember after completing a course in biology. Tyler (1930) found that high school biology students forget facts with great rapidity. On the contrary there was little or no loss (after eight months) in the ability to explain everyday phenomena and to generalize from given facts. Tyler (1933) studied the permanence of student learning following a course in elementary college zoology. After a 15-month period it was found that specific information, represented by naming animal structures, was the most quickly forgotten; there was little loss in the ability to apply zoological principles to new situations or to interpret data obtained from experiments. Wert (1937) studied the permanence of learning from elementary college zoology one, two and three years after completion of the course. He found that after a three-year period students would receive a failing grade if they were required to retake the examination given at the time they completed the course, if the same standards were used. However in the ability to apply principles of zoology to new situations he found no loss over the three-year period.

Weissman (1946) used six high school biology classes as an experimental group and six other classes as a control. He found that with the proper methods students could be taught to interpret biological data and to think critically, but to obtain these results a course must be organized around problems and class activities of a problem-solving nature used. Pupils in the experimental class learned more facts and biological principles than the students taught in the conventional manner (a course developed within the logical organization of the subject). Weissman concluded that "the direct teaching of interpretation of data is considerably more effective than teaching that regards this objective as merely concomitant."

Owens (1949) investigated, using experimental and control high school biology classes, the relationships between the ability of students to recognize scientific principles in test situations and the ability to apply these principles to problematic situations. He found that students in classes where specific instruction on the applications of principles to new situations is given show increased ability in this respect compared with students in classes where the instruction is not so directed.

Downing (1933 and 1936) found that "skill in scientific thinking" is not a by-product of the study of scientific subjects as courses are ordinarily taught. Higgins (1942) explored the educability of high school biology students in situations calling for the use of inductive methods. The experiment was conducted by instruction on the "scientific method" with special consideration given to the factors which are involved in formulation of hypotheses and generalizations. The instructional material consisted of 30 biology experiments selected from scientific journals. He found that the instruction resulted in meaningful gains in the "ability to classify conclusions, to write more complete conclusions, to write with less rationalization, to make fewer statements directly contradicted by the data and to sense patterns in the data."

Crall (1950) in a controlled experiment with high school biology students, found that students taught through a procedure which required them to apply principles made greater growth in this regard than students taught by the ordinary classroom methods. The investigator notes that both groups made improvements in the ability to apply biological principles but that the direct approach (experimental group) was more effective.

Caldwell and Lundeen (1930) noted that high school students possess many unfounded beliefs about science. They found that specific instruction directed toward the correction of certain unfounded beliefs associated with heredity resulted in a more desirable attitude. The permanence of the changed attitude was not determined. The investigators felt that many science misconceptions exist simply because there has not been instruction that would inform pupils otherwise.

Bingham (1939), using equated high school biology classes, sought to determine the effectiveness of two procedures in teaching nutrition. The *experimental* classes were taught nutrition principles with specific application to man's well-being and the use of the knowledge in intelligent action. The *control* classes were taught nutrition principles without any conscious teaching emphasis on the application of these principles. A variety of test measures were used including tests a year following the completion of the courses. The data favored the experimental group and indicated that teaching could be directed to enable students to apply their knowledge of nutrition.

Bond (1940) used college freshman classes in genetics to study the effectiveness of a teaching procedure stressing the application of principles of genetics. Experimental and control classes were established. The experimental group was taught with particular attention to the practical applications of the principles of heredity and the control class was taught in the traditional manner. Tests were constructed to measure student progress in the attainment of facts about genetics, the ability to apply the principles of genetics and the ability to use scientific methods of thinking. The control group surpassed the experimental group in one area of subject matter; the experimental group rated higher in the ability to apply their knowledge to practical problems. The results imply that students in general education courses in genetics can be taught so as to effect changes in their thinking and, indirectly, their attitudes.

Urban (1944) used experimental and control classes in high school biology to study behavioral changes resulting from a study of communicable diseases. He found that ignorance about communicable diseases and unsanitary behaviors can be overcome through proper instruction. Also that changes in overt behavior can be attained. Urban concludes that, while there may be a loss in information, over a period of time the changes in the direction of desirable behaviors seem to be more permanent.

Subarsky (1948) compared the relative effectiveness of an experimental and conventional procedure for administering high school biology and social studies classes with reference to the development of desirable attitudes regarding discriminatory social practices. Biology and social studies classes met together to consider biologically and historically valid concepts and to provide a better oppoɪ ʌity to integrate the physical and cultural aspects of human relations. He found, by means of tests, that there was a significant positive change in attitude in the combined classes which was not present when biology and social studies classes were taught separately. Solomon and Braunschneider (1950) using control groups of college level biology students sought to determine if attitudes related to ethnic, racial, religious and nationality groups would shift as a result of teaching structured to apply the methods of science to such prejudicial attitudes. They found that instruction designed to apply the "scientific method" to problems of prejudice did not produce a positive effect on social attitudes of the kinds investigated.

Mohler (1950) developed a special mental hygiene unit of instruction to be used in biology classes. The experimental unit was built around the needs and desires expressed by biology students in the field of mental hygiene. Classes were taught the unit using regular group instructional techniques. He found that the students' faulty knowledge was corrected and that they gained new insights into their behavior.

A number of investigations have been carried out to determine better ways of organizing the content of biology courses to obtain improved learning. Gilbert (1910) studied two methods of presenting a beginning course in college zoology; an "economic" and a "pure science" approach. His measures of achievement were: 1) assimilation of zoological knowledge; 2) ability to experiment and to interpret the results; and 3) student interest in the course. He found a slight advantage on all measures, particularly student interests, favorable to the "economic" approach.

Winier (1951) in a study on the organization of college biology courses came to the conclusion that it was easier to justify a course developed around personal-social needs than to defend a strictly logical course in terms of subject-matter.

Hunter (1921) explored three methods of presenting high school biology using a rotation technique with the classes. The procedures tested were 1) the lecture method; 2) the textbook method; 3) and a developmental method (an experimental or problem technique applied orally in the classroom). Measures of achievement were: immediate recall of content, retention, and the development of power to answer thought questions. The developmental method, where students had more freedom to define and discuss problems, seemed to give the best result both with respect to retention and the ability to handle thought questions. The lecture method was most effective for immediate recall, the developmental method was next and the textbook method showed the greatest loss in retention. Hunter found that a teacher's preference for a particular method generally produced better results with that method.

Laton (1929) conducted a controlled experiment in teaching high school biology in which she consciously applied principles of learning psychology to the arrangement of class procedures. She found that the effectiveness of student learning was greatest in those classes where the teaching methods had been planned in terms of established psychological procedures.

Wrightstone (1934) reviewed the theories of curriculum development, *circa* 1930, and found two viewpoints: 1) *a conven-*

tional procedure—consisting of the presentation of topical and logically organized minimum essentials of knowledge and skills from a discipline; 2) *a newer viewpoint*—providing for an integration or synthesis of topics to encourage an expansion of the present interests and experiences of pupils. Wrightstone used two paired groups of biology students equated on a number of factors to test experimentally the two curricular theories. *The conventional class* was taught by the usual lecture-textbook-recitation technique, visual aids were used, but most of the work was from the textbook. In the *experimental class* (newer viewpoint) student work was centered around individualized problems or projects, the use of museums, botanical gardens, field studies and current biological literature. In measurable outcomes (standardized biology tests scores) the experimental group was statistically better. The experimental group developed a greater ability to use library resources, current periodical literature and did more writing and illustrating.

Anderson, Montgomery and Ridgway (1951) conducted a pilot study to discover the relative value of various multisensory methods for teaching high school biology. Four teaching groups were established: 1) *a control group,* taught by traditional methods; 2) *a film group,* taught mostly by films but with no laboratory work and minimum use of demonstrations; 3) *a laboratory group,* taught by the use of specimens and many dissections, but without films; and 4) *a combined film-laboratory group.* A standardized biology test was used to measure achievement differences between the groups at the conclusion of the investigation. The combined film-laboratory group was significantly superior in achievement; the difference between the other groups was not significant.

Simon (1953) studied the teaching methods used by high school biology teachers and found that among 77 teachers, demonstration-discussion techniques, lectures, and test-recitation were the most often cited methods. Laboratory work was not considered a primary method for teaching biology; only 3% of the teachers stated the method was frequently used, while

34% classify it as a less commonly used technique. Individualized methods, projects and research-problem approaches were used by 1% of the teachers. Older experienced teachers were more inclined to lecture and teachers rated as *conservative* by a jury spent two-thirds of their teaching time in a lecture-textbook-recitation routine. Teachers rated *progressive* by a jury spent 69% of their teaching time in laboratory work, projects, or demonstrations and also had more students entering science fairs. Simon noted that the methods rated as the most effective by teachers were not the methods they actually used most commonly.

Newman (1957) compared the effectiveness of three methods of teaching high school biology: 1) a lecture-discussion and outside reading assignments method; 2) lecture-discussion and in-class reading assignments; 3) lecture-discussion and no reading assignments. None of these methods were found statistically superior, either for bright or slow students. Students with a low I.Q. and low in reading ability were more successful in the group where lecture-discussion and in-class reading were used.

Magruder (1936) sought to determine whether the idea of photosynthesis could be taught if the structural detail of the leaf was considered at a separate time. She found that whether structural detail preceded or followed the study of photosynthesis made no difference in the student's learning as measured by the test used.

Downing (1931) attempted to determine the length of time needed to teach certain principles of biology to the point of mastery under ordinary classroom conditions. It would appear that it takes about four weeks to develop a principle to the point that a student can make applications from it.

Friedenberg (1949) investigated the feasibility of developing with college biology students an insight into the differences between the content and structure of the discipline. He found that instruction could be managed to foster the student's insight into the organization and viewpoint of the biological sciences.

Hurd (1954) analyzed 1,373 articles written by science teachers on problems of teaching and found that little use appears to be made of established principles of learning in the teaching of science. The teachers were most cognizant of 1) individual differences; 2) the relation of student interest to learning; and 3) the importance of direct practice in developing problem-solving skills.

Summary

The objectives of a liberal education in biology at both the high school and college levels include an expectation that the students' attitudes toward social and personal problems and toward science will be modified as a result of instruction. The research seems to indicate that: 1) instruction in biology can change student attitudes in a pre-determined direction provided the teaching material and classroom methods are designed specifically to achieve the particular attitude, and 2) a favorable attitude is not a concomitant result of instruction in the related subject content.

The research on teaching methods is limited and inconclusive for valid recommendations about specific techniques. Few of the studies make clear the objectives sought for and in other instances the investigator confined his judgment of achievement to "facts" accumulated, or a limited interpretation of the outcomes of science teaching. The following hypotheses about science teaching appear to have support:

1. Methods which most actively involve the learner appear to be the most effective for the acquisition and retention of learning.

2. The logical organization of biology courses in terms of the historical development of its conclusions does not seem to result in the most effective learning.

3. The permanence of student learning in biology courses is dependent to some degree upon the extent to which he is able to conceptualize his knowledge.

XIV

Instructional Resources for Teaching Biology

SCIENCE TEACHERS have assumed that laboratory work is an essential part of biology instruction, and that a non-laboratory course is not really a science course. School administrators have questioned the educational returns from laboratory work in terms of the extra costs in both time and money. Most of the literature on biology laboratory work is of the "how-to-do-it type" with very little on "why-do-it." It has been repeatedly suggested that films, slides, charts, models and teacher demonstrations could effectively replace laboratory work in biology, since it is not of an investigatory nature as now taught.

Martin (1952) in a survey of 768 high schools found that in 97.7% of the schools the biology courses required laboratory work of some kind. The procedures most often used in conducting the work were: 1) small group experiments, 26.2%; 2) individual laboratory work, 20.2%; 3) pupils paired for experiments, 19.0%; 4) teacher demonstrations, 15.5%; 5) pupil observation in classroom, 5.9%; 6) pupil demonstrations, 2.2%; and 7) other, 1%. In 39.7% of 768 high schools the biology experiments were pupil-teacher planned; in 28.8% the experiments found in a workbook or manual were used; in 19.8% of the schools teacher-prepared guides were used; 5% of the teachers used experiments found in the textbooks; 5% reported a problem-solving approach and 1.7% used some other source.

Martin (1952) found that 36.6% of the schools had a regularly scheduled period for biology laboratory work; 35.2% used an integrated laboratory-recitation period and 28.2% reported a flexible laboratory schedule. Only 88 of 768 high schools had a double period for biology laboratory work. In Barnes' (1959) survey of 1,876 high schools it was found that 25.8% of the schools had double laboratory periods for science courses; biology classes were not reported separately.

Martin (1952) obtained responses from 637 high schools on percent of time devoted to biology laboratory work, and found it to be approximately 26.4% with a range from 2% to 75% of total class time. Johnson's (1950) survey of 531 high schools showed that 331 of 62.5% reported scheduled time for laboratory work.

Richardson (1945) in a review of problems faced by beginning science teachers found that most have a very limited conception of the function of the laboratory in the learning situation. Littrell (1950) investigated the laboratory practices and the objectives of high school biology in Nebraska. He found that while most teachers thought laboratory work was an important part of instruction they were unable to relate the teaching objectives to the activities of the laboratory.

Cunningham (1934) found that students who had individual laboratory work in high school biology did superior work in college botany but there seemed to be no effect on their performance in zoology courses.

In a survey of student reactions to high school biology, Klise and Oliver (1947) found that the students wished they had more field trips and experiments in their biology course.

Cooprider (1926) conducted an experiment to determine the effectiveness of biology laboratory exercises when demonstrated by the teacher and when demonstrated by the pupil. He found that: 1) the pupils' average test scores favored teacher demonstrations; 2) students preferred teacher demonstrations; 3) well supervised pupil demonstrations were about as effective as the teachers'; and 4) exercises requiring much explanatory discussion were better done by the teacher. Murray (1950) designed a series of demonstrations for high school biology courses based upon biological principles. Smith (1952) found that biology teachers in one county used demonstrations more frequently than individual laboratory procedures.

Atkins (1936) using three pairs of equated groups of high

school biology students conducted a controlled experiment to determine whether an increase in factual knowledge and interest in laboratory work are better obtained through conventional laboratory procedures than laboratory methods involving a considerable measure of student self-direction. The conventional group (control) did teacher assigned experiments from mimeographed laboratory directions and recorded their drawings and experimental results in notebooks. The self-directed (experimental) group worked under a plan of teacher-pupil planning of individual projects for which the student assumed most of the responsibility for his own investigative procedures and selected his own sources for reference. The findings were: 1) students in the experimental group learned as much factual knowledge as those in the control group; and 2) the self-directed group also read more widely, were more enthusiastic and had a greater curiosity. Atkins noted that high school students need to be given careful training in working on their own before they are allowed to proceed on a self-direction plan.

There are about forty investigations comparing the effectiveness of individual laboratory work versus lecture demonstrations in terms of various learning outcomes from science instruction. Only a limited number of these studies were in biology. Cunningham (1920), in a controlled experiment, found that students in high school botany learned 7% more from laboratory demonstrations than from individual laboratory. He also found that the demonstration method saved 30% of class time over the individual method. Cunningham (1924) repeated his experiments and found that the results favored the lecture-demonstration method both in economy of time and immediate recall of facts. The data showed that results were not consistent for all experiments or for all students. He concluded that generalizations cannot be made about a best type of laboratory teaching.

Cooprider (1923) studied four methods of conducting high school biology laboratory work: 1) demonstrations with oral instructions; 2) demonstrations with written instructions; 3) individual work with oral instructions; and 4) individual work with written instructions. His measure of student achievement was a delayed recall test. He found that 1) oral instructions produced somewhat better results than written for both individual and demonstration work; 2) "individual work with instruction is more efficient than demonstration work with oral instruction" 3) "demonstration work with written instructions is more efficient than individual work with written instructions"; 4) demonstration work was slightly better than individual experiments; 5) individual experiments consumed twice as much class time and were more costly than demonstration work. Cooprider notes that the usual procedures for presenting biology laboratory work contribute little to teaching the student to reason scientifically.

Johnson (1928) equated classes in high school biology and experimented with different methods of laboratory instruction. He used three laboratory procedures: 1) lecture demonstration; 2) group laboratory—four or five students working together; and 3) individual laboratory. Johnson concludes that, although it cannot be conclusively stated the demonstration method is superior, it does yield returns equal in primary learning when compared with a group taught by the individual method.

In 1946, Cunningham summarized 37 research studies on lecture demonstration versus individual laboratory work in science teaching. The summary includes eight studies on biology teaching; the others are in the physical sciences. The biology investigators are not separated in Cunningham's summary but they are not in contradiction to the results for the physical sciences. The summary given here is briefed from Cunningham's complete report. He first reviewed and evaluated the reliability of the 37 studies, the research techniques used, the appropriateness of the controls, the adequacy of data, the measures of achievement, the investigator's interpretation of his results, and the reactions of critics to the various studies. Following this analysis he developed the following hypotheses regarding laboratory procedures in science instruction:

(1) When ordinary written information tests are to be used in the evaluation of the results of teaching and when all other important

factors in the teaching situation are, or can be made, favorable, consider the use of the lecture demonstration method if: the learning involved in connection with the exercises is complicated and difficult; the apparatus used is complicated, difficult to manipulate, or expensive; the apparatus used is sufficiently large to be seen at a distance; the pupils are likely to make mistakes when working alone in determining and interpreting the results after an exercise has been completed; a large amount of subject matter must be covered in a limited time.

(2) When ordinary written information tests are to be used in the evaluation of the teaching results and when all other important factors in the teaching situation are, or can be made, favorable, consider the use of individual laboratory work if: the exercises are short and easy—not complicated as to learning involved or apparatus used; caring for individual differences seems especially desirable; the results can be easily seen and interpreted, by the pupils working alone, after the exercise has been performed. There are some data which indicate that the individual laboratory method may have merit in easy laboratory exercises even though they extend over a rather long time—especially if several observations must be made over a period of days. A few data were found which indicate that girls made a little better use of the individual laboratory method than boys.

(3) Teachers should consider doing a high proportion of the laboratory exercises by the individual laboratory method if one important objective is the development of laboratory skills.

(4) Teachers should consider doing a high proportion of the laboratory work by the individual laboratory method, without specific directions, if one important objective is the development of ability to solve *laboratory* problems.

(5) Teachers should consider doing a high proportion of the laboratory work by the individual laboratory method when one important objective is the development of laboratory resourcefulness.

(6) The use of both methods in a science course will make for greater variety of experiences and therefore increased interest on the part of pupils.

(7) General ability in scientific thinking is so complicated—made up of so many different steps with certain safeguards necessarily surrounding each step—that both methods can probably be used to advantage in its development. Much more analytical work is neces-

sary in order to determine the points in the complicated procedure at which a particular method can make the greater contribution.

Hunter (1922a) investigated the relative values of a visual and an oral instruction method in demonstration and experimental work in elementary biology. In the *visual method* the teacher avoided oral work, writing all instructions on the board. In the *oral method* the teacher developed the problem by asking questions and through discussion. Slow learning students benefited most by the oral method and all students were benefited more by the *oral* than the *visual* procedure. Hunter (1922b) sought to determine the relative values of: 1) *oral questioning* and *discussion* combined with *demonstrations*; and 2) a method in which the problem is worked out *individually*, guided solely by directions in the manual. "Based on comparative marks, the *oral* laboratory lesson was far superior to the laboratory manual lesson."

Anderson (1950), in a survey of the practices of 58 Minnesota high school biology teachers, found that in 65% of the cases laboratory work paralleled classwork and in 5% of the cases laboratory instruction preceded equivalent classwork. Fifty-five percent of the biology teachers followed a laboratory manual or workbook. Only 11% of the teachers used laboratory experiments to illustrate or to provide practice in the use of the methods of science.

Anderson (1949) examined the achievement scores of 1,980 biology students and found that they achieved more in biology when the number of laboratory hours was in the upper quartile of the state distribution. Whether the laboratory instruction preceded, accompanied, or followed class discussion was not significant in pupil achievement in biology.

Laboratory work in biology has been the subject of criticism by most of the curriculum committees reporting on the teaching of biology. In the popular literature more articles are written by teachers about laboratory work than any other topic. The research appears to indicate that the assumed values of laboratory work in biology, such as: 1) increasing the powers of observation; 2) acquiring factual information; and 3) clarifying the understanding of structures through visualization, are obtained equally well, and often more economically, by other techniques than individual laboratory methods.

New biology laboratory exercises and experiments have been produced in recent years which provide resources for modifying and extending laboratory opportunities in biology. These are reported in the following publications:

1. Morholt, Evelyn, Brandwein, Paul F., and Alexander, Joseph. 1958. *Teaching High School Science: A Sourcebook for the Biological Sciences.* Harcourt, Brace and Company. New York. 506 p.
2. Munzer, Martha E., and Brandwein, Paul F. The Conservation Foundation. 1960. *Teaching Science Through Conservation.* McGraw-Hill Book Company, Inc. 470 p.
3. National Academy of Sciences—National Research Council. 1960. *Laboratory and Field Studies in Biology.* Holt, Rinehart and Winston, Inc. New York. 281 p.
4. National Academy of Sciences. 1960. *Laboratory and Field Studies in Biology (Teacher Edition).* Holt, Rinehart and Winston, Inc. New York. 199 p.
5. Weaver, Richard L., Project Leader. 1955. The National Association of Biology Teachers. *Handbook for Teaching of Conservation and Resource-Use.* Interstate Printers and Publishers, Inc. Danville, Illinois. 499 p.
6. Weaver, Richard L., Editor. 1959. The National Association of Biology Teachers. *Manual for Outdoor Laboratories: The Development and Use of Schoolgrounds As Outdoor Laboratories for Teaching Science and Conservation.* Interstate Printers and Publishers, Inc. Danville, Illinois. 81 p.

The Biological Sciences Curriculum Study developed a "block" approach in laboratory teaching which provides opportunities for young people to learn the skills and processes of science through active participation in scientific investigation with some depth. New experiments were also devised that require a wider use of living organisms.

A good laboratory program requires suitable facilities and

equipment. Martin (1952), in a survey of 558 schools, found that in 95 schools out of 100 where biology is taught one can expect to find running water, sinks, electric outlets and a gas supply. A demonstration table and storage cases were available in most schools. Pupil laboratory tables were found in 361 out of 439 high schools. Barnes (1959) found from a survey that: of 1,876 high schools offering biology, 84.9% had a teacher demonstration table; 59.5% had student tables fitted with services; 30% had wall counters with services; 85.9% had storage cabinets; 74.3% had gas; 87.9% had water; 85.7% had alternating current and 27.7% had direct current.

Both Martin (1952) and Barnes (1959) gathered data from high schools on the availability of compound microscopes and microprojectors. Martin found that 91% of the schools teaching biology had compound microscopes available for the course. The number available was in direct relation to the size of the high school. His data suggest that the number of microscopes even in the larger schools was far from adequate. Barnes, using a standard of one microscope for each two students, found 6 in 10 high schools do not meet the standard in any biology classroom. He found that 47.2% of the large high schools did meet the standard. Microprojectors were available for *all* rooms in 60.5% of the small high schools and in at least 70.0% of all schools there is a microprojector in at least *some* room. Martin's survey showed that 78% of the schools had hand lenses for use in biology classes.

Martin's study (1952) included a survey of projection equipment owned by biology departments: 67% were found to own sound film projectors; 58.2%, slide projectors; and 29.5% had silent film projectors. He also found that film strips were used regularly by more teachers than either motion picture or 2" x 2" slides, approximately two-thirds of all teachers used some motion pictures in biology instruction; but only 37.8% of the large schools, compared with 84.3% of the small high schools, used them regularly. More than 70% of the biology teachers made regular use of: charts, preserved specimens, microscope slides, posters and pictures, and living specimens as part of the instruction.

The development and design of laboratory facilities has been studied by Munch (1952), Hurd (1954), Richardson (1954), and Johnson (1956).

The Council of Chief State School Officers (1959) developed a listing of biology equipment suitable for secondary school courses. Barnes (1935) sought to determine the standards, factors or criteria which control the selection of special equipment, supplies, apparatus, specimens, and other materials used in the teaching of biology and other sciences. After compiling the opinions of 120 specialists in science education the following criteria for the selection of science teaching materials were considered important by at least 60% of the specialists: 1) its contribution to the attainment of the objectives of science instruction; 2) its suitability for studying science principles; 3) its appropriateness for the type of laboratory work used—demonstration or individual experiments; 4) its cost; 5) its suitability for student use; 6) its relation to the requirements of the course and experiments done.

There are many resources outside of the classroom valuable for teaching of biology. The availability and use of these resources has been studied by several investigators. Bailey (1950) found that biology teachers made somewhat more use of community resources than teachers of chemistry and physics. Science teachers, however, made little use of visiting scientists, student interviews with scientists or surveys of the community. Hibbs (1956) studied the use of outdoor laboratories in teaching natural resources and conservation, and found them to be unequaled in learning opportunities for these topics. Peterson (1952) studied the resources of a fresh water stream as an outdoor laboratory to present principles encompassed in pre-college science and conservation programs. Hollenbeck (1958) in a stratified random sampling of high school seniors, found that few had had an opportunity for outdoor science experiments.

Coady (1950) found that 60% of the national parks and 87% of the municipal, state and county parks surveyed had nature trails. She also found that nature trails were on the decline due to vandalism. Martin (1952) found that among 769 high schools

66 (8.4%) had a nature trail; 60 (7.6%) a school forest; 53 (6.7%) a school museum; 47 (6.0%) a school farm; 38 (4.8%) a garden; 11 (1.4%) a camp; and 69 schools had other resources for biology teaching, such as, a small lake, an enclosed court with growing plants or a large vivarium. Barnes (1959) obtained replies from 1,876 secondary schools concerning teaching resources for biology. He found that supplementary resources were available in the following percent of schools: a nature preserve, 12.8%; a school forest, 9.8%; a school farm, 8.1%; a school camp, 1.3%; a garden plot, 14.3%; and a science museum, 11.7%. A third to a half of the schools appear to have none of these facilities, and the larger high schools had a wider variety of facilities, with the exception of school forests, farms, preserves and gardens, than small schools. These outdoor teaching areas are more likely to be found available in junior high schools than in senior high schools.

Martin (1952) obtained replies from 485 schools regarding the use of field trips and excursions. A total of 61.7% of the schools reported that field trips were a regular part of the biology instruction. The average number of trips was 5.2% and was about the same for small or large schools. However, when the average number of trips taken annually by the biology classes in schools of different sizes was compared with the average number of sections of general biology, the number of trips was inversely proportional to the size of the school. Schools with 1–99 enrollment took 5.1 trips per section, in large schools of 500 or more pupils the average number of trips was 0.6 per section. In 38% of the schools it was reported that no field trips were taken by biology classes.

Johnson and Kerwean (1952) surveyed 49 eastern high schools about the availability of greenhouses for teaching high school biology. They found 19 of the schools had a greenhouse, but seldom was it equipped with temperature, humidity or light controls. Martin (1952) in a survey of 769 high schools found that 70 or 8.9% had a greenhouse available for instructional purposes, however, the percentage was 17.9 in the larger high schools.

Barnes (1959) found in a sample of 1,876 high schools that 10.3% had a greenhouse, but that among the larger high schools the percentage was 30.9.

A much discussed question in biology teaching has been the educational value of student-made drawings in terms of the amount of time required to produce them. Ayer (1916) studied retention and other psychological values with reference to laboratory drawings in high school. He concluded that laboratory drawings did not contribute to analytical study but tended to encourage bad habits of thinking. The excessive use of representative drawings created a distaste for science, produced copyists and failed to aid the memory. Cooprider (1925) found that high school biology students who finished their drawings in ink did somewhat better on examinations (52.1%) covering the exercise than those who used pencil (46.8%). The extra time required for inking appeared to be the only argument against inking. Alpern (1936) compared the effectiveness of student-made and prepared drawings in college biology classes. He found that the labeling of prepared drawings and the procedure of making original drawings were equally effective with regard to the students' acquisition and retention of the factual information derived from laboratory work. The time saved by the use of prepared drawings would rate it the more efficient procedure. Tobler (1945) found that high school biology students who were required to label prepared drawings made better scores on examinations of factual learning than equated groups of students who prepared and labeled their own drawings. Ballew (1928) investigated the learning effectiveness of two laboratory procedures in high school zoology. One group of students were required to make representative drawings of structures observed while a second group simply located the same structures on the specimen without drawing them. The data showed that the construction of representative drawings does not aid the pupil in making analytical observations nor did it contribute to remembering the observations made in the laboratory, either upon immediate or delayed testing.

Wallin (1954) investigated the teaching values of commercially prepared versus original laboratory drawings. He found that students who labeled and used commercially printed drawings equaled or surpassed the achievement gain in factual knowledge made by students who completed and labeled detailed free-hand drawings.

Heubner (1929) studied the relative effectiveness of models, charts and teachers' drawings as aids in learning botanical structures by high school students. She found that students, both bright and slow, made greater gains in factual knowledge with the aid of models and teachers' drawings than with charts. Richter (1956) attempted to determine whether certain personality components of the student influenced the extent of their learning from drawings. She found a small, but significant, correlation between "goodness" of drawings and the quality of learning of biological subject matter.

Kiely (1951) compared the learning value of student-made drawings and photomicrographs in pre-professional biology courses. He found that students, both low and high I.Q., learned and retained more factual information and could identify accurately more structures from laboratory work when photomicrographs were used.

Stathers (1933) compared the use of the microprojector with the individual microscope as a learning aid in high school biology. His results showed that when identical materials were presented by the two methods the students who had been taught with the microprojector made higher scores, both in correct answers to questions and in the labeling of test drawings, than those who had used microscopes. Stathers concludes that a saving of 50 to 75% of laboratory time can be effected by the use of the microprojector compared with the individual microscope. Brechbill (1940) in a similar study found no statistically significant differences in student learning between those using the microscope and those instructed with a microprojector, although the microprojector group made higher scores on the tests. The majority of students favored the microprojector over the microscope.

The use of films as instructional aids in teaching has been extensively studied; however, the number of studies referring specifically to the use of biology films is limited. Rulon (1933) studied the use of sound films in science teaching; some of his films included biological materials. He found that the teaching effectiveness in science could be increased as much as twenty percent, measured in terms of learning retention, when films were used in combination with modern teaching methods. Keeslar (1945) studied the extent to which a number of films contributed to the major objectives of secondary school science: 1) understanding of scientific principles; 2) understanding of the elements of the scientific method; and 3) development of scientific attitudes. He found that only five percent of the scenes in the films examined contributed to any of the three selected objectives.

Knowlton (1948) surveyed 24 of the largest public school systems in the country regarding the use of teaching films. He found science teachers were having difficulty using films and were particularly critical of the content of science films.

Wise (1949) found that when biology films were used in an appropriate manner and in a reasonable number, and when the content was closely related to the course they did not detract from normal school accomplishments.

Smith (1949) investigated the relationship between intelligence and the learning which results from the use of educational sound motion pictures. He found that films did not produce superior learning with either bright or dull students. Smith and Anderson (1958) found that films increased the learning of biological principles more than facts. Anderson et al (1956) found that "a choice of films in harmony with the objectives of instruction in a particular academic area is capable of yielding superior results in learning if the proper choice of films is accompanied by realistic film utilization with selected objectives of instruction in an academic area." The investigators stressed the need for films produced in harmony with the objectives of biology teaching.

Mallinson (1952) found that biology teachers appear to use

films to a greater extent than teachers in other fields. Their greatest problem was obtaining the films when they were needed. Twenty-nine percent of the teachers criticized the films in biology for errors and many felt that the vocabulary used was too advanced for the typical high school pupil.

Most science educators are of the opinion that the teaching of biology could be improved through the use of more supplementary reading materials. Anderson (1949) surveyed the reading materials of the 56 Minnesota high schools and found the median number of scientific magazines available to students was less than two. Twenty-six percent of the teachers felt they had an adequate supply of books. Martin (1952) found in a sampling of 786 high schools that the smaller schools had approximately three science magazines available for pupil use and the typical large high school, five. From a total of 105 schools, 13.3% reported they had no magazines available for pupil use; 9.7% of these were large high schools and 15.5% were schools under 500 enrollment.

Stafford (1952), using equated clases in high school biology, taught one group from a textbook and the other with supplemental materials arranged in the same order as the topics in the textbooks. He found that neither group was superior to the other on the examinations used.

Clubs, project work and other student activities are presumed to be of value in learning science. The extent of these activities has been studied but their contribution to learning has had little attention. Martin (1952) found that 33.5% of 786 secondary schools offering general biology had science clubs but only 27 schools reported clubs which were exclusively "biological" in nature. He also found that among the 531 high schools where projects were used that in 29.4% of the schools they were a required part of the class work but were optional in the remaining schools. Martin's survey showed that 67.2% of 777 high schools made use of some method of supplementing instruction in biology, such as, participation in: 1) science exhibits, 42.0%; 2) talent search contests, 33.7%; 3) science fairs, 24.6%; 4) youth science congresses, 5.9%; and 5) other, 6.1%.

Beck's (1957) survey showed that biological exhibits in science fairs were less frequent than those in physical science. Martin (1952) found that 70.2% of the biology students in 528 high schools visted science fairs.

Summary

The interpretation of the studies on individual laboratory work versus laboratory demonstrations is dependent upon the assumptions one makes about the purposes of laboratory instruction. If an exercise is simply to acquire a knowledge of facts or to reinforce their retention one procedure is as good as the other. The choice of a particular method, an individual experiment or a demonstration, is a question of economy either in time or cost. Economy favors the use of laboratory demonstrations more than individual work.

On the other hand, if it is assumed that a student learns to understand the nature of science through "sciencing," then intuitively it seems necessary that the student be involved in an investigative or research activity. Under these conditions he is engaged in planning experiments, collecting and managing data, formulating results, interpreting his "conclusions" and subjecting these to further verification or criticism. The success of the student *and* the effectiveness of the experiment are judged in terms of how effective was the exercise in developing critical thinking and providing experience in the "ways" of science. Measures of this sort were not generally used in comparing individual laboratory work with teacher demonstrations, although some researchers were cognizant of them. One is forced to conclude from the research on laboratory work in biology courses that if the objectives are to understand science, or to acquire knowledge the usual observational exercises, drawings, and "cookbook-type experiments" have produced disappointing results.

The teaching facilities for biology classes in high school leave something to be desired. Speculations about needed improvements should be accompanied by studies of the extent to which present resources are being used.

Much of the data in this chapter reveals the kind and extent of the teaching tools a biology teacher has available. More studies are needed to determine the extent to which these teaching resources are used, for what educational purposes and how effective they are in terms of student learning. The results of these studies would also suggest some of the responsibilities of a teacher education program.

XV

Unresolved Problems in Biological Education

AT VARIOUS TIMES during the past sixty years science committees with a membership of high school teachers, educators and
scientists have made recommendations for the improvement of
high school biology teaching. At no time does it appear that any
committee had more than limited or local influence on either
course content or teaching practices. Throughout the past two
decades and more sharply in the past five years, there has again
been serious criticism of the science offerings in the secondary
school. New committees have been established to explore the
problems and to develop modern courses and materials for the
teaching of biology.

Generally, the criticism of American secondary school science
has been that it is "anti-intellectual," "soft," "behind the times,"
"too much oriented toward the student" (life adjustment), that
it "fails to teach real science," and that it does not meet the demands of a scientifically and technologically oriented society.
Suggestions for the improvement of education in the sciences
are that it be made "more rigorous," that it must "be up-dated,"
and develop a better understanding and an appreciation of the
scientific enterprise.

The educational crisis of the fifties stimulated many suggestions for curriculum improvement in science and some experimentation. A few critics would look to the European secondary
schools for a solution to the curriculum problems of American
high schools. Others seek a solution in the educational patterns
of the "good old days."

There are those who feel that if science teachers were better
trained the problems of science education would be solved. This
statement was also made by the science committees of the 1895–

1900 period; the recommendation then was that they should be "as well-trained as mathematics and history teachers." There seems to be no valid explanation of why biology teachers should be considered more poorly trained than other teachers when all are subject to the same general types of training programs. Not a few biologists have stated flatly that the problem results from the "overwhelming number of education method courses required leaving no time for training in science content." But the national average and median of professional courses for the training of science teachers in 1960 was 18 semester units out of the 120–122 required for graduation with a third of the education units granted for teaching biology as an intern teacher. It also appears from the data available that less than half of the biology teachers have had a course in the methods and techniques of science teaching.

Other critics have suggested that it is the quality of the science courses given teachers that is at fault. Yet close to 70% of all biology teachers are graduates of liberal arts colleges and universities and less than 10% are graduates of normal schools. Those biology teachers who graduate from state colleges in most instances have had their biology from instructors who obtained their doctorates in the biology departments of universities. It is disappointing however that in the majority of colleges and universities the most distinguished research scientists—the men who know science best—are the most inaccessible for the training of high school teachers of biology.

Another assumption has been that teachers of biology are simply not up-to-date in their field and therefore the best kind of science teaching is not possible. Hundreds of institute programs have been developed in the past decade to bring them up to date. Frequently teachers have found difficulty in relating the very latest in scientific achievement to courses for high school students, few of whom will seek careers in science. Then again, "frontiers in knowledge" are generally the most difficult even for the research scientists and the special value for high school teachers is not always apparent. The results of recent scientific research are always available in the literature should teachers or textbook writers desire to use it.

Considerable data have been amassed to show that many teachers of biology did not major in the subject and have had little training. This is true, and represents a weakness in state certification laws or a laxity in school administration policies. If a person is assigned to teach a subject for which he lacks training the fault lies with the local school administrator and the school board members. Frequently, however, their only alternative, with the present shortage of science teachers, is either to abandon the biology courses or accept an unqualified teacher. The development of teaching films in biology and Federal assistance to provide science supervisors and to support in-service training programs represent stop-gap measures to do the best that is possible short of dropping the course from the curriculum.

Another step for improving education in biology has been to enlist research biologists to develop new high school courses. Some of the observations made by scientists about existing courses have been: 1) there is more content than can be taught with understanding in the time allowed; 2) there are concepts and theories of science more significant that those now being taught; 3) there is need for more emphasis on science as a process of inquiry; 4) there is need for a greater emphasis on developing an appreciation of the scientific enterprise; 5) the technological or applied topics should be illustrative of basic principles rather than centers of instruction; 6) laboratory work should be more investigatory and experimental in nature; 7) the course content could be more interesting; 8) courses need to be more "open-ended" and less authoritarian, and 9) biology concepts capable of being taught with understanding at earlier grade levels should not be duplicated in high school courses. With these ideas in mind both local and national biological curriculum committees have sought to invent improved courses.

As the committees for the development of "modern" biology courses get under way it may be useful to explore some of the weaknesses of earlier groups, those between 1895 and 1950. Sufficient time has passed to give perspective to their work and to allow an evaluation of the programs they conceived. The following statements represent a consensus of reactions from many sources and for none of the committees are all the comments appropriate but all committees are represented.

1. The scientist is interested only in having the high school deliver an "embryo" scientist to his freshman course in the university. While they have seen the need and decry the lack of scientific literacy on the part of the general public, they do not typically outline courses in science suitable for *all* the students who make up this population.

2. The scientist develops high school courses as professional courses for scientists and condemns existing courses as too vocational and representing only technologies. His stated objectives are those of a liberal education, the course he produces is more suited to professional education.

3. Some curriculum workers see the applied aspects of science as more closely related to the lives of people than "pure" science. Atomic power, conservation, personal and public health, and the "population explosion," for example, are of widespread concern while the processes used by scientists in arriving at the basic causes underlying these problems seem less generally valuable. It has been difficult to develop science courses that have appeal and interest for the typical high school student and which at the same time provide him with an intellectual understanding of the discipline. A balanced "picture" of the interrelation of science and technology has not been achieved in secondary school science courses by any curriculum group.

4. While many scientists wish students to know something of the methods of science and to appreciate it as the "grand adventure," they see this as possible only by the "doing of science." Other scientists feel that this cannot be achieved under the artificial conditions of a high school laboratory or even in undergraduate college courses. The question is one of whether the typical student can develop some knowledge and appreciation of the scientific endeavor without engaging in an investigation. In one sense this is equivalent to asking whether one can understand and appreciate something of good lit-

erature and music without being able to write either. In both science and the arts there are degrees of sophistication and intellectual insight, but curriculum committees in the past have not accepted this assumption, nor have they developed teaching materials with this viewpoint in mind.

5. In the past, science committees have not sought to develop a science curriculum but have been satisfied to build courses. The sub-committees on science of the "Committee of Ten," (1893) and of "The Commission on the Reorganization of Secondary Education," (1918) did seek to organize all science courses around a set of objectives common to secondary education. The "Commission on Secondary School Curriculum," (1938) came the nearest to defining a curriculum in science. A biology course has particular contributions to make to one's education in science as well as to his total intellectual development.

6. Major changes in curriculum design and new ways of teaching science have been proposed by committees without a public statement as to why it was felt new directions were desirable and why a particular path was chosen. Consequently teachers who were expected to teach the "new" courses and the school administrators who had to explain the advantages of the "new" course over the "old" to the general public were without guidance. To state that the new objectives are apparent in the content of the proposed course is not very helpful to those who are inexpert in science curriculum design. Those preparing new science courses have at times worked for several years discussing a rationale for their approach and then overlooked the fact that the classroom teacher has not had the benefit of such discussion and therefore needs a clear and definitive statement of perspectives. This problem has been further intensified by the divergent points of view about secondary school science teaching among scientists. Those scientists who publish most widely on "the value of science in contemporary life," and the various national commissions considering science teaching are seldom in sufficient accord to allow a clear statement of policy. There are scientists who stress "the social function of science" and "science for responsible citizenship" and others who believe science should be studied for its own sake and discount the broader social and educational functions. The majority of curriculum committees have failed to debate this issue sufficiently to define the place of science in the education of the "man on

the street." The "pure" or "basic" scientists and the "applied" scientists or "technologists" have defined the goals for secondary school science teaching differently. There were those who wrote about the scientific enterprise who felt that any such distinctions were "purely academic." Then there were those who would accept only a definition of "science" that was limited to its intellectual activities. A high school course in biology would not be of the same character if developed under one or the other of these points of view. Curriculum makers in science have so far not been able to compromise these points of view, nor have they developed courses in either "pure" or "applied" science. It appears we are now reaping the results of this confusion, illustrated by erroneous beliefs found in the minds of the general public about what is science and what is not science. This also helps to explain the curious hodge-podge of content found in biology courses.

7. Curriculum planning is best done when the nature of learning is considered at the time courses are under development. The research in this area is extensive and has much to suggest for curriculum organization. That the majority of committees on biology teaching have not taken advantage of the research on learning is evidenced by the neglect of integrative themes in course planning, the extensive array of detailed facts presented without conceptual order, the routine and sterile nature of the laboratory work suggested.

8. A major weakness in the work of biology curriculum committees for the past half century, and it is quite possible that this may account for the limited influence of their efforts, has been a consistent failure to directly recognize that the measure of course improvement is to be found more in improved methods of teaching than in the re-assortment and re-alignment of subject content. The "new" courses outlined by each committee could always be taught in the same manner as the old although this was seldom the intent of the planning group. Better teaching has mostly to do with the performance of the teacher and the ways in which he manages the content of a course. Teaching science as inquiry, for example, is more a matter of classroom procedures and the organization of learning than the selection of the content although the structure of material is of definite advantage. This is to say that the updating of courses per se does not assure the improved teaching of biology.

Summary

Following the close of World War II it was apparent that secondary school education in America, particularly instruction in science, was in need of change and should be critically re-examined. The work of the American Association for the Advancement of Science, Cooperative Committee; the National Society for the Study of Education report on *Science Education in American Schools*; The Steelman report on *Science and Public Policy,* and the Harvard Committee's statement on *General Education in a Free Society* are illustrative of the diverse groups interested in the problem. These and other reports of the period were explicit in stating that the scientific-technological culture in America has progressed to the point where a different education in science, one more suitable for modern times, is demanded.

In the decade following these reports, 1950–1960, the emerging social, economic, political, and technical developments intensified the concerns about the science curriculum. Developments which initiated the "space age" caused the American public to view the teaching of science in secondary schools as having reached a crisis. The immediate result was the establishment of a series of national committees sponsored by the National Science Foundation and other groups to develop new ends and new content in science more appropriate to the educational needs of this generation.

The situation in which the present science committees must work has dimensions that are different from those of even a few years ago. Some of these are:

1. Nearly all young people now go to high school and graduation from high school is seen as the "common school education" in the minds of the American people. The diversity of interests and abilities among students today is greater than high school teachers have ever before experienced. Existing curricula in science are unsuited to many students. The gifted student, the "science prone" and the slow learner find little challenge in the science courses as they are now organized.

2. With the rise in secondary school attendance there has been an increased demand for collegiate education and a third of the high school graduates now enter college. This is an amount double that of the previous generation. Only a small fraction of these students will major in science and technical fields—a number estimated as being too small for the demands of a scientific and technically oriented society—but it does mean that a larger number of students than ever before will have an opportunity for science courses and at a higher maturity level. The need to plan the biology curriculum from the first through the sixteenth year of school is now apparent.

3. The situation described as the "explosion in scientific knowledge," which can be illustrated by the 50,000 scientific and technical journals now in print and the publication of over 1,250,000 research articles per year, complicates the problem of curriculum construction. There is more knowledge in every field than even a specialist can digest in a lifetime. The crucial problem is how do we provide an entrance to this knowledge by the non-specialist? What should be the sampling of available biological knowledge for the few hours that a high school science teacher will have with a student? The productive life of the young people now in school will extend to past the year 2000; most of the significant concepts for their life have not yet been announced or discovered. Under the impact of science and technology the world has changed more and faster than in any other twenty-year period in history. The expectation is that the next twenty years will witness even greater changes. Planned programs of research and development have shortened the time between basic discoveries and their application in ways that touch the life of every person. Research in science reaches the layman more quickly than at any other time in history. The present programs of science education are not adapted for conditions of rapid change and progress. Curriculum makers have not had to meet this problem before and innovations in curriculum design are in demand.

4. There are few who would question the extensive influence science has had on contemporary intellectual life and thinking. Yet the intellectual aims of science instruction have to a large extent been absent in secondary school teaching. The ramifications of science into almost every aspect of living and its impact upon the life of every individual demands that nearly everyone have an intellectual understanding of the scientific enterprise.

5. The results of research on human learning indicate that the teaching of science must provide for more conceptual learning than it has in the past. The rate at which science information is forgotten by students suggests that a more efficient and useful approach to the organization and presentation of science must be found. The communication of science has become a major concern in our society and poses many problems for a scheme of science education.

The biology courses under development for high school must be different from those of the past because the student population, science and the culture are different. The increasing complexity of science and of society demands more efficient learning to meet the problems of the future. Science curriculum committees of the Sixties need to seek innovations both in course construction and in teaching.

XVI

Problems and Issues in Biology Teaching

MANY GROUPS of scientists and educators have explored the problems of biological education since the turn of the century and considerable research has been done to find useful procedures in managing the problems. The renewed efforts to improve biology teaching indicate that there are many issues and problems yet to be resolved. Some of these problems are of long standing, others have emerged only recently. Problems and issues, yet unrecognized, can be expected to arise as new knowledge and theories are announced in biology, as the social scene changes and as the philosophical assumptions underlying science education reflect changes in both the scientific and social communities. Each generation must expect that it has a responsibility to examine and to modify the purpose and process of education in the sciences to suit its own time.

The present efforts to improve the "quality" or "excellence" of science teaching have accentuated the following problems and issues:

1. How can the process of biological inquiry be taught to high school students? What changes would be needed in classroom and laboratory procedures? The resolution of this problem would seem to lie primarily in the way biology courses are taught. Teaching and textbooks which focus almost entirely on the conclusions of science allow few opportunities for the student to experience the intellectual aspects of science. Laboratory work that is concentrated on verification rather than investigation is also at fault.

2. Now that science has penetrated our culture at nearly every point and has become imperative in the education of *all* people there is need to re-think the theoretical constructs underlying education in the sciences. Biology teaching has typically been oriented too much in terms of the needs of biologists rather than for the intellectual understanding it could provide the non-specialists. It may be

238

that much knowledge useful to the research biologist is also valuable for the average citizen but it will not be for the same reasons. Most curriculum committees in the past have been more aware of the scientist's needs than the citizen's needs. To what extent is it necessary to develop different kinds of courses in order to provide a satisfactory education in biology for *all* students? Should the criteria for the selection of content for each course differ? What should be the qualitative differences in courses for the gifted student? The frequently used plan of simply providing more work, longer assignments, or reading from college textbooks would not seem to meet the intellectual standards of work appropriate for a superior student.

3. The varying purposes for the teaching of biology imply special approaches to learning. Suggestions about the strategy of learning science are limited and the extent to which use is made of existing research is negligible. The rote learning now so common in biology teaching needs to be directed toward learning of a conceptual nature and which leads the student to some understanding of the structure of the subject. How this may be accomplished is in need of much study and research.

4. What should be the relationship of high school biology to college biology? Courses at both levels are quite similar and duplicate each other at many points. The trend toward advanced biology courses in high school has led many teachers to adopt college general biology textbooks for these courses. It is questionable whether this is the best kind of "advanced" training in high school. Little has been done to define the biological concepts, insights, appreciations or the thought processes suitable to an advanced high school course. Is it to develop a higher level of biological sophistication based on the typical tenth grade course or an orientation to new topics?

5. Has the subject field approach to building biology courses, as it has been practiced, outlived its usefulness? The continual resifting of the content of the special fields of biology to make high school courses can only produce progressively shallower courses resulting from the sheer volume of new knowledge. Can there be a synoptic approach for the non-specialists, a "science of life," with topics chosen and organized in a way to represent the main stream of biological thought? The building of courses around integrative themes, represented by the work of the Biological Sciences Curriculum Study, is one approach to the problem.

6. There is the question of the value of developing a science curriculum in high school without sharp distinctions between biology, chemistry and physics. This would make it possible, for example, to include more bio-physics, surface chemistry and biochemistry in the biology course and more biology in physics and chemistry. One part of the problem is to bring together the knowledge that belongs together for understanding biological processes and to eliminate needless duplication in high school. The demands for more efficiency in education and the extent of available knowledge both suggest we can no longer afford useless repetition between courses.

7. The demand for *technicians* in every field of science raises the question as to whether it is the function of the high school to provide this training. The problem deserves study both in terms of the need and the suitability of present courses for this purpose whether the training is done in the secondary school or at a higher level.

8. The problem of obtaining an adequate number of biology teachers and the question of how they shall be trained remains. The biological training of teachers at present is more suited for research than for teaching and is inadequate for either. Then there is the question of how modern procedures for teaching science, new curriculum development, and research on science teaching can be brought to the attention of classroom teachers. Much study is needed on the problem of communication within the field of biological education. The trend toward a wider use of science supervisors and consultants provides avenues for the introduction of new curricula and laboratory materials through in-service programs. There is also the need to develop college programs for teaching that are specifically designed to provide a *continuing* education in biology on a broad front.

9. The textbook in biology, as an educational tool, is in need of study. The present efforts to develop biology courses that are less authoritarian must also be reflected in the textbook since it functions as the curriculum in most schools. More fundamental is whether the structure of textbooks, as they are now known, is of the kind that is most useful in helping young people along the way where the concern in science education is upon intellectual aims.

10. How can the participation of classroom teachers be enlisted to carry on the professional research required to improve secondary school science teaching? There is need for studies on the teaching of

biology carried out under normal classroom conditions by teachers trained in experimental procedures.

11. There is the problem of developing an integrated program of biology from kindergarten through the twelfth grade. It appears logical that the organization should follow a sequence of conceptual levels representing a deeper understanding of a particular biological concept as the pupil progresses through the grades. There is need for considerable research at this point to determine whether there is a sequence in understanding biological concepts and at what points of maturity various concepts can be successfully introduced.

12. Usually a student's success in a course is judged largely by his ability to accumulate and repeat an array of discrete facts. Recent committees on the teaching of science have recommended that objectives, such as, "understanding science" and "the nature of inquiry" be given priority as a measure of achievement in courses. Curriculum movements in the past lost much of their potential effectiveness because after setting new goals they provided no means of student evaluation beyond that of factual recall, like the committees before them. Regardless of the emphasis established by successive curriculum committees, the student had only to continue as usual to pass the course.

13. A curriculum plan is needed which makes it possible for high school courses to keep pace with the significant developments in biology. Course revisions at intervals of ten to twenty years or "crash" programs during a time of educational crisis have not produced a satisfactory curriculum except for the moment. A continuing committee of research biologists is needed to identify the significant concepts of their field as they are developed. Then a corresponding body of science educators and teachers experienced in curriculum engineering is needed to develop up-to-date teaching materials as the need is apparent. The responsibility for a proper biology curriculum would lie with both groups.

14. There has been some interest in the development of a national curriculum in biology. The nature of the content of biology and the local availability of teaching material suggest that a specific course is not an answer to the problem; however, outlines built around significant biological concepts and common teaching objectives offer a promise of commonality without destroying individuality in biology teaching. It seems to many educators that there should be some

reasonable expectations from any student who lists a biology course successfully passed on his record.

15. The many unanswered questions about effective classroom teaching procedures suggests a need for a systematic plan of research. Some of the research problems would be better investigated in the departments of biology, some in schools of education, and others in psychology departments. Particularly is there a need for support and coordination for this kind of endeavor. The complicated nature of problems in learning and teaching requires research projects of considerable magnitude and duration. It is essential that problems of education in science be attacked with the same vigor and support as questions of science.

16. Laboratory work has been a distinguishing and highly regarded feature of biology courses but the educational values have not been clearly demonstrated. The facilities and equipment of the high school laboratory were copied from the research laboratories of the universities but its purposes were omitted. If a laboratory is defined as a place where scientists "do science," this is seldom its function in high school. Students do not typically leave the laboratory with a better understanding of the nature of scientific inquiry or a "feeling of discovery." The development of the BSCS "block" plan is an innovation that promises to restore some measure of the original intent of laboratory work.

17. It is expected that citizens in a democracy should be capable of taking intelligent action on socially significant problems. Schools are expected to provide an understanding and information on these problems, for example, conservation, population growth, food supply, health, radiation and others. How should these matters be handled within the framework of high school biology to enable young people to become informed?

18. It is assumed that the best kind of biology teaching requires adequate facilities in terms of library references, laboratory and demonstration equipment, project and growing areas, audio-visual materials and other teaching aids. Facilities and equipment need to be designed in terms of what is done in the high school and for the purposes which guide high school courses. There has been only limited study of teaching resources and the particular value of each for the improvement of learning in biology.

19. It is becoming increasingly apparent that the present organization of teaching schedules and the size of high school classes may not

be the most efficient. A redeployment of time to allow for some periods that are longer for special laboratory exercises, field trips and other activities is needed. Films and certain demonstrations might well be used with 150 students instead of 30 if class schedules were more flexible. Trained teacher aides and laboratory assistants would increase not only the professional services of the teacher but result in better teaching.

20. Biology teachers generally have available to them a wide range of community resources for instructional purposes; meadows and vacant lots; museums, aquaria and zoos; birds and insects; ponds, rivers and streams; forests, dunes and deserts; greenhouses and landscaping; pets and gardens; and a variety of research biologists, agriculturists, bacteriologists, medical men, and others to use as class speakers and consultants on projects. The use of these resources and people appears to be limited and is secondary to preserved materials, models, charts and pictures. There are many opportunities in biology teaching to have students deepen their understanding of science through experiments and projects carried on at home. The student's home and yard can be utilized as an extension of the biology classroom. The problem is that teachers of biology have not been trained to use the living resources of the environment for instructional purposes.

Summary

The problem and issues of biology teaching are extensive possibly more so than a decade or two ago. This does not mean there has been a lack of progress in biological education but simply that the conditions in our culture, biology and education have changed radically in recent years. This is not the world of the 1940's or even of the 1950's; we should not expect that the answers to problems in the past decade are entirely pertinent today. The objectives and curriculum for biology teaching in the Sixties may be quite out-dated by 1970; progress in biological thinking and discovery will make sections of present courses of small educative value; they may even be misleading in another decade.

We must continually seek better definitions for the meaning of a basic education in the biological sciences. And all that we know for certain is that the answers are not found in the past although there are signals that may prove useful.

BIBLIOGRAPHIES

Bibliography of Committee Reports

(Chapters 1 through 8)

1. *Advancing Biology Education. Recommendation and Activities of the Committee on Educational Policies, 1954–1957.* 1957. National Academy of Sciences–National Research Council. Division of Biology and Agriculture. Washington, D.C.
2. AIBS-BSCS. *High School Biology, Blue Version.* 1960. BSCS. Boulder, Colorado.
3. AIBS-BSCS. *High School Biology, Green Version.* 1960. BSCS. Boulder, Colorado.
4. AIBS-BSCS. *High School Biology, Yellow Version.* 1960. BSCS. Boulder, Colorado.
5. AIBS-BSCS. 1960. *High School Biology, Blue Version. The Laboratory, Part One.* BSCS. Boulder, Colorado. p. ix–xi.
6. AIBS-BSCS. 1960. *High School Biology, Teacher's Commentary. Part One.* BSCS. Boulder, Colorado.
7. *American Biology Teacher.* 1960. "Microbiology in Introductory Biology." 22:(5) Special Issue.
8. American Council on Education. 1940. *What the High Schools Ought to Teach.* Washington, D.C. 36 p.
9. Armacost, Richard and Klinge, Paul, Co-editors. 1956. "Report of the North Central Conference on Biology Teaching." *The American Biology Teacher.* 18 (1):4–72.
10. Beauchamp, Wilbur L. 1932. *Instruction in Science.* Bulletin 1932, No. 17. National Survey of Secondary Education. Monograph No. 22. Washington, D.C. 63 p.
11. Behnke, John, Chairman. 1957. *Criteria for Preparation and Selection of Science Textbooks.* Committee on Educational Policies. National Academy of Sciences–National Research Council. Washington, D.C. (Also found in the *AIBS Bulletin,* 1957, 7:26–28)
12. Bessey, Charles E. 1896. "Science and Culture." *Addresses and Proceedings,* National Education Association. Washington, D.C. 35:939–942.
13. Bigelow, M. A., Chairman. Committee Appointed At the Request of the American Society of Zoologists. 1906. "College Entrance Option in Zoology." *School Science and Mathematics.* 6:63–66.
14. Brandwein, Paul. From a letter addressed to biologists, from the chairman of the BSCS Gifted Student Committee. March 15, 1960.
15. Breukelman, John and Armacost, Richard, Co-Chairman. Publications Committee. 1955. "Report of the Southeastern Conference on Biology Teaching." *The American Biology Teacher.* 17(1):4–55.

16. Caldwell, Otis W., Chairman. 1909. "A Consideration of the Principles That Should Determine the Courses in Biology in the Secondary Schools." *School Science and Mathematics.* 9:241–247.
17. Caldwell, Otis W., Chairman. 1914. "Preliminary Report of the Committee on a Unified High School Science Course." *School Science and Mathematics.* 14:166–168.
18. Caldwell, Otis W., Chairman. 1915. "Report of the Central Association of Science and Mathematics Teachers Committee On a Unified High School Science Course." *School Science and Mathematics.* 15:344–346.
19. Caldwell, Otis W., Chairman. 1920. *Reorganization of Science in Seconday Schools.* Commission on Reorganization of Secondary Education. Bul. 1920. No 26. Department of Interior, Bureau of Education. Washington, D.C. 62 p.
20. Caldwell, Otis W., Chairman. 1924. "American Association for the Advancement of Science, Committee on the Place of the Sciences in Education." *Science.* 60:536–540.
21. The Commission on the Reorganization of Secondary Education. 1918. *Cardinal Principles of Secondary Education.* Bul. 1918, No. 35. Department of Interior, Bureau of Education, Washington, D.C. 32 p.
22. Commission on Secondary School Curriculum. 1938. *Science in General Education.* A Report Prepared by the Science Committee. Appleton-Century Co. New York. 579 p.
23. *Committee on Educational Policies.* 1955. Report of Fifth Meeting, June 30. National Academy of Sciences–National Research Council. Washington, D.C.
24. Committee on Educational Policies, Division of Biology and Agriculture. 1958. *Suggestions for a Comprehensive Program for Improving the Content of Biology Programs from Elementary School to College.* National Academy of Sciences–National Research Council, Washington, D.C. (mimeo)
25. *Conference on Biological Education.* March 10, 1953. National Academy of Sciences–National Research Council. (mimeo) Division of Biology and Agriculture. Washington, D.C.
26. Crosby, Clifford. 1907. "Physiology, How and How Much." *School Science and Mathematics.* 7:733–744.
27. Croxton, W. C., Chairman. 1942. *Redirecting Science Teaching in the Light of Personal-Social Needs.* The American Council of Science Teachers, National Education Association. Washington, D.C.
28. Dewey, John. 1916. "Method in Science Teaching." *General Science Quarterly.* 1:(1):3.
29. Dexter, E. G. 1906. "Ten Years' Influence of the Report of the Committee of Ten." *The School Review.* 14:254–269.

30. Downing, Elliot R. 1928. "The Biology Course Outlined in Major Objectives." *School Science and Mathematics.* 28:498.

31. Downing, Elliot R., Chairman. 1931*a*. "The Teaching of Biology." North Central Association Quarterly. 5:395–398.

32. Downing, Elliot R. 1931*b*. "Teaching Units in Biology—An Investigation." *North Central Association Quarterly.* 5:453–470.

33. Educational Policies Commission. 1944. *Education for All American Youth.* National Education Association. Washington, D.C. 421 p.

34. Galloway, T. W., Chairman. 1910. "Report of the Committee on Fundamentals of the Central Association of Science and Mathematics Teachers." *School Science and Mathematics.* 10:801–813.

35. Ganong, W. F. 1910. *The Teaching Botanist.* The Macmillan Co. New York. 270 p.

36. Glennan, T. Keith. 1960. "New Order of Technological Challenge." *Vital Speeches.* 36:237.

37. Hall, E. H., and Committee. 1898. "Memorandum Concerning Report of Committee of Sixty." *Addresses and Proceedings, National Education Association.* Washington, D.C. 37:964–965.

38. Hargitt, C. W. 1905. "Place and Function of Biology in the Secondary Schools." *Education.* 25:475–487. (Quoted from Christy, Otto B. 1936. "The Development of the Teaching of General Biology in the Secondary Schools." *Journal of the Tennesee Academy of Science.* 12:(3):181.)

39. Havighurst, R. J. et al. 1943. "High School Science and Mathematics in Relation to the Manpower Problem." *School Science and Mathematics.* 43:138–141.

40. Hunter, George W. 1923. "Report of the Committee on a One-Year Fundamental Course of Biological Science." *School Science and Mathematics.* 23:656–664.

41. Hunter, George W. 1934. *Science Teaching at Junior and Senior High School Levels.* American Book Co. New York. 552 p.

42. Hunter, George W., Chairman. 1938. "Report of Committee on Secondary School Science of the National Association for Research in Science Teaching." *Science Education.* 22:223–233.

43. Kingsley, Clarence D., Chairman. 1911. "Report of the Committee of Nine on the Articulation of High School and College." *Addresses and Proceedings, National Education Association.* Washington, D.C. 49: 559–567.

44. Lark-Horovitz, K. 1945. "The Teaching of the Basic Sciences." *Science Education.* 29:148–151.

45. Lark-Horovitz, K. 1948. "Science Teaching Today." A Summary of the Report of the Cooperative Committee on the Effectiveness of Science Teaching. *The Science Teacher.* 15:61–62.

46. Lark-Horovitz, K. 1950. The Cooperative Committee for the Teaching of Science—Report to the AAAS Council, December 1949. *Science.* 111: 197–200.

47. Lawson, C. A. Conference Director. Committee on Educational Policies, Division of Biology and Agriculture. 1957. *Laboratory and Field Studies in Biology: A Sourcebook for Secondary Schools.* Preliminary Edition. National Academy of Sciences–National Research Council, Washington, D.C.

48. Lawson, Chester A. (Editor), Paulson, Richard E. (Assistant Editor). 1960. *Laboratory and Field Studies in Biology.* Holt, Rinehart and Winston, Inc. N. Y. 281 p.

49. Lawson, Chester A. (Editor), Paulson, Richard E. (Assistant Editor). 1960. Teacher Edition, *Laboratory and Field Studies in Biology.* Holt, Rinehart and Winston, Inc. N.Y. 500 p.

50. Lee, Addison E. and Spear, Irwin. 1960. *Plant Growth and Development.* BSCS. Boulder, Colorado. p. ii–iv.

51. Linville, H. R., Chairman. 1909. "The Practical Use of Biology." *School Science and Mathematics.* 9:121–130.

52. Linville, H. R. 1910. "Old and New Ideals in Biology Teaching." *School Science and Mathematics.* 10:210–216.

53. Mayfield, John C. Conference Director. 1960. *Using Modern Knowledge to Teach Evolution in High School.* The University of Chicago, Chicago, Ill. 36 p.

54. Moore, John A. 1960. "A Statement of the Objectives of the BSCS." *BSCS Newsletter* 3. p 2.

55. Morse, M. W. 1911. "Elementary Biologies." *Science.* 33:430–433.

56. Munzer, Martha E., Brandwein, Paul. 1960. *Teaching Science Through Conservation.* McGraw-Hill Book Co., Inc. 469 p.

57. National Academy of Sciences–National Research Council. Division of Biology and Agriculture. Committee on Educational Policies. *Report of the Sub-Committee on Pre-College Education, Fourth Meeting,* March 5–6, 1955 (mimeo)

58. National Academy of Sciences–National Research Council. Division of Biology and Agriculture. Biology Council. Committee on Educational Policies. *Proceedings of the Sixth Meeting.* September 5, 1955. (mimeo)

59. National Association of Secondary School Principals. 1944. *Planning for American Youth: An Educational Program for Youth of Secondary School Age.* National Education Association, Washington, D.C. 63 p.

60. National Education Association. U.S. Bureau of Education. 1893. *Report of the Committee on Secondary School Studies—Report of the Committee of Ten.* Washington, D.C.

61. Natural Science—A Report Authorized by the Central Association of

Science and Mathematics Teachers. 1941. *Subject Fields in General Education*. D. Appleton-Century, Inc. New York. p. 115–135.

62. Neal, Nathan A., Chairman. 1942. *Science Teaching for Better Living— A Philosophy or Point of View*. The American Council of Science Teachers, National Education Association. Washington, D.C.

63. Nightingale, A. F., Chairman. 1899. "Report of the Committee on College Entrance Requirements." *Addresses and Proceedings*, National Education Association. Washington, D.C. 38:625–630.

64. Noll, Victor H., Chairman. 1947. *Science Education in American Schools*. Forty-Sixth Yearbook of the National Society for the Study of Education, Part I. University of Chicago Press. Chicago, Illinois.

65. "On the Place of Science in Education." 1928. A report presented to the Council of the American Association for the Advancement of Science at the Second Nashville Meeting December 1927 by the Special Committee of Science in Education. *School Science and Mathematics*. 28:640–664.

66. Peabody, James E., Chairman. 1915. "Preliminary Report of the Biology Subcommittee On the Reorganization of Secondary Education." Nation Education Association. *School Science and Mathematics*. 15:44–53.

67. Peabody, J. E., and Committee. 1916 "Revised Report of the Biology Committee of the National Education Association Committee on the Reorganization of Secondary Education." *School Science and Mathematics*. 16:501–516.

68. Persing, Ellis C. 1924. "Report of the Committee on Reorganization of the Biological Sciences, Appointed by the Cleveland Biology Teachers Club." *School Science and Mathematics*. 24:241–246.

69. *The Place of Science in the Education of the Consumer*. 1945. A statement prepared for the Consumer Education Study of the National Association of Secondary School Principals by the National Science Teachers Association. National Education Association. Washington, D.C. 32 p.

70. Powers, Samuel R., Chairman. 1932. *A Program for Teaching Science*. The Thirty-First Yearbook of the National Society for the Study of Education, Part I. Public School Publishing Co. Bloomington, Illinois, 364 p.

71. Powers, Samuel R. 1941. "The Work of the Bureau of Educational Research in Science." *School Science and Mathematics*. 41:7–9.

72. "Report of the Committee on Biology." 1905. *School Science and Mathematics*. 5:50–52.

73. Report of the Harvard Committee. 1945. *General Education in a Free Society*. Cambridge, Massachusetts. Harvard University Press. 267 p.

74. Report of the Sub-Committee on Biology. 1927. "Report of the Committee on Standards for Use in the Reorganization of Secondary School Curriculum." *North Central Association Quarterly*. 1:510–514.

75. Riddle, Oscar. 1906. "What and How Much Can Be Done in Ecological and Physiological Zoology in Secondary Schools." *School Science and Mathematics*. 6:212–216; 247–254.
76. Riddle, Oscar, Editor. 1942. *The Teaching of Biology in Secondary Schools of the United States*. Union of American Biological Societies. 76 p.
77. Roney, H. Burr. 1959. "A New Approach to the High School Biology Course." *The AIBS Bulletin*. 9:(2):18–20.
78. Schwab, Joseph J. 1960. "A Statement of the Activities of the BSCS." *BSCS Newsletter 3*. p. 3.
79. Steelman, John R., Chairman. 1947. The President's Scientific Research Board. *Manpower for Research*. Vol. IV. *Science and Public Policy*. Appendix II.
80. Stevens, Russell B. 1956. *Career Opportunities in Biology*. Row, Peterson and Company. Evanston, Illinois.
81. Stone, Dorothy F. 1959. *Modern High School Biology*. Bureau of Publications, Teachers College, Columbia University, N.Y. 96 p.
82. "Symposium on the Function and Organization of the Biological Sciences in Education." 1908. *School Science and Mathematics*. 8:536–551.
83. Weaver, Richard L., Project Leader. 1955. *Handbook for Teaching Conservation and Resource-Use*. The Interstate Printers and Publishers Inc. Danville, Ill. 499 p.
84. Weaver, Richard L., Editor. 1959. *Manual for Outdoor Laboratories*. Interstate Printers and Publishers, Inc. Danville, Ill. 81 p.

Bibliography of Research Studies

(Chapters 9 through 16)

Alpern, Morris L. 1936. "A Comparative Study of the Effectiveness of Student-Made, and Prepared Drawings in College Laboratory Work in Biology." *Science Education.* 20:24–30.

Anderson, Kenneth E. 1949*a*. "Adjuncts to Science Instruction." *School Science and Mathematics.* 49:475–476.

Anderson, Kenneth E. 1949*b*. "Summary of the Relative Achievements of The Objectives of Secondary School Science in a Representative Sampling of Fifty-Six Minnesota Schools." *Science Education.* 33:323–329.

Anderson, Kenneth E. 1950. "The Teachers of Science in a Representative Sampling of Minnesota Schools." *Science Education.* 34:57–66.

Anderson, K. E., Montgomery, Fred S., and Ridgway, Robert W. 1951. "A Pilot Study of Various Methods of Teaching Biology." *Science Education.* 35:295–298.

Anderson, K. E., Montgomery, F. S., Smith, H. A., Anderson, D. S. 1956. "Toward a More Effective Use of Sound Motion Pictures in High School Biology." *Science Education.* 40:43–44.

Atkins, Wesley Converse. 1936. *Some Probable Outcomes of Partial Self-Direction in Tenth-Grade Biology.* Doctoral Dissertation. Princeton University Press. Princeton, New Jersey.

Ayer, Fred Carleton. 1916. *The Psychology of Drawing with Special Reference to Laboratory Teaching.* Doctoral Dissertation. Warwick & York, Inc. Baltimore, Maryland. 186 p.

Bailey, Doyle E. 1950. *The Use of Community Resources by High School Science Teachers.* Doctoral Dissertation (Unpublished) Colorado State College of Education.

Ballew, Amer M. 1928. "A Comparative Study of the Effectiveness of Laboratory Exercises in High School Zoology with and without Drawings." *The School Review.* 36:284–295.

Barnes, Cyrus W. 1935. "Criteria for the Selection of Science-Teaching Materials." *Science Education.* 19:152–157.

Barnes, David H., Project Director. 1959. *Mathematics and Science Teaching and Facilities.* Research Monograph 1959-M1. Research Division. National Education Association. Washington, D. C.

Beck, Charles F. Jr. 1957. *The Development and Present Status of School Science Fairs.* Doctoral Dissertation (Unpublished) University of Pittsburgh.

Bentley, Carvel M. 1934. *A Study to Determine Those Biological Principles*

Which Most Frequently Appear in the Public Press. Master's Thesis. (Unpublished) University of Michigan.

Bergman, George J. 1947. "A Determination of the Principles of Entomology of Significance in General Education." *Science Education.* 31:23–32; 144–157.

Bingham, Nelson E. 1939. "Teaching Nutrition in Biology Classes—An Experimental Investigation of High School Biology Pupils in Their Study of the Relation of Food to Physical Well-Being." *Science Education.* 23:188–194.

Blanc, Sam S. 1958. "Biology Interests of Tenth and Eleventh Grade Pupils." *Science Education.* 42:151–159.

Blanc, Sam S. 1957. "A Topical Analysis of High School Biology Textbooks." *Science Education.* 41:205–209.

Blanchet, Waldo E. 1946. *A Basis for the Selection of Course Content for Survey Courses in the Natural Sciences.* Doctoral Dissertation. (Unpublished) University of Michigan.

Bond, Austin D. 1940. *An Experiment in the Teaching of Genetics, with Special Reference to the Objectives of General Education.* Doctoral Dissertation Contributions to Education, No. 797. Teachers College, Columbia University. New York.

Brandwein, Paul F., Watson, Fletcher G., and Blackwood, Paul E. 1958. *Teaching High School Science: A Book of Methods.* Harcourt, Brace and Company. New York. p. 239–240.

Brechbill, Edith. 1941. "A Study of a Microprojector as a Teaching Aid." *Science Education.* 25:215–218.

Bunce, George. 1952. *A Study of How High School Graduates Who Have Not Entered College Evaluate Their High School Science Courses.* Master's Thesis. (Unpublished) Ball State Teachers College, Muncie, Indiana.

Burdick, John Gordon. 1960. *A Study of Cross-Section Drawings Used as Technical Illustrations in High School Science Textbooks.* Doctoral Dissertation. (Unpublished) Syracuse University. Univ. Microfilms. Ann Arbor, Mich. (Dissertation Abstr. 20:2707)

Caldwell, Otis W., and Lundeen, Gerhard E. 1939. "Investigation of Unfounded Beliefs." p. 280–291. In, *Third Digest of Investigations in the Teaching of Science*—by Francis D. Curtis. P. Blakiston's Son and Company, Inc. Philadelphia.

Caldwell, Otis W., and Lundeen, Gerhard E. 1930. "Investigations of Unfounded Beliefs." *Journal of Educational Research.* 22:257–273.

Caldwell, Otis W., and Weller, Florence. 1932. "High School Biology Content as Judged by Thirty College Biologists." *School Science and Mathematics.* 32:411–424.

Chappelear, Claud S. 1929. *Health Subject Matter in Natural Sciences.* Contributions to Education No. 341. Doctoral Dissertation. Teachers College, Columbia University. New York.

Christy, Otto B. 1936. *The Development of the Teaching of General Biology in the Secondary Schools.* Doctoral Dissertation. Peabody Contribution to Education No. 201. George Peabody College for Teachers.

Coady, Martha. 1950. *A Survey of Trailside Museums and Nature Trails.* Master's Thesis. University of Massachusetts.

Cooprider, J. L. 1923. "Laboratory Methods in High School Science." *School Science and Mathematics.* 23:526–530.

Cooprider, J. L. 1925. "Shall the Drawings Be Inked?" *School Science and Mathematics.* 25:62–73.

Cooprider, J. L. 1926. "Teacher Versus Student Demonstrations in High School Biology." *School Science and Mathematics.* 26:147–155.

Council of Chief State School Officers. 1959. *Purchase Guide for Programs in Science, Mathematics, Modern Foreign Languages.* Ginn and Company. Chicago. 336 p.

Crall, Howard William. 1950. *Teaching and Evaluation of Achievement in Applying Principles in High School Biology.* Doctoral Dissertation. (Unpublished) Ohio State University.

Cretzinger, J. I. 1941. "An Analysis of Principles or Generalities Appearing in Biological Textbooks Used in the Secondary Schools of the United States from 1800 to 1933." *Science Education.* 25:310–313.

Crowell, Victor L. 1937. "Attitudes and Skills Essential to the Scientific Method, And Their Treatment in General-Science and Elementary-Biology Textbooks." *School Science and Mathematics.* 37:525–531.

Cunningham, Bert. 1934. "A Study of the Effect of a Course in High School Biology on Performance in College Biology." *School Science and Mathematics.* 34:578–588.

Cunningham, Harry A. 1920. "Individual Laboratory Work versus Lecture Demonstration." *University of Illinois Bulletin.* 18:105–107.

Cunningham, Harry A. 1924. "Laboratory Methods in Natural Science Teaching." *School Science and Mathematics.* 24:709–715, 848–851.

Cunningham, Harry A. 1946. "Lecture Demonstration versus Individual Laboratory Method in Science Teaching—A Summary." *Science Education.* 30:70–82.

Curtis, Francis D. 1924. *Some Values Derived from Extensive Reading of General Science.* Doctoral Dissertation. Contributions to Education, No. 163. Teachers College, Columbia University, New York.

Dawson, Jean. 1909. "Essentials of Biology in the High School." *School Science and Mathematics.* 9:653–657.

DeLoach, W. S. 1941. "The Scientific Articles in a Popular Magazine." *Science Education.* 25:273–274.

Downing, Elliot R. 1933. "Does Science Teach Scientific Thinking?" *Science Education.* 17:87–91.

Downing, Elliot R. 1936. "Some Results of a Test on Scientific Thinking." *Science Education.* 20:121–128.

Downing, Elliot R. 1931. "Teaching Units in Biology—An Investigation." *North Central Association Quarterly.* 5:453–457.

Fay, Paul Johnson. 1930. *The History of Science Teaching in the American High Schools of the United States.* Doctoral Dissertation. (Unpublished) Ohio State University.

Finley, Charles William. 1926. *Biology in Secondary Schools and the Training of Biology Teachers.* Doctoral Dissertation. Contributions to Education No. 199, Teachers College, Columbia University. Bureau of Publications. New York.

Finley, Charles W., and Caldwell, Otis W. 1923. *Biology in the Public Press.* Lincoln School of Teachers College. New York. 151 p.

Fitzpatrick, Frederick Linder. 1937. "Pupil Testimony Concerning Their Scientific Interests." *Teachers College Record.* 38:381–388.

Fribourgh, James H. 1957. *Recommended Principles and Generalizations for an Introductory Biology Course in the Junior College.* Doctoral Dissertation. (Unpublished) State University of Iowa.

Friedenberg, Edgar Z. 1949. "The Measurement of Student Insight into the Structure Underlying the Organization and Viewpoint of the Biological Sciences." *Science Education.* 33:57–64.

Gilbert, J. P. 1910. "An Experiment in the Teaching of Biology." *The Nature Study Review.* 6:78–80.

Glidden, Harley F. 1956. "The Identification and Evaluation of Principles of Soil and Water Conservation for Inclusion in the Secondary School Curriculum." *Science Education.* 40:54–78.

Henderson, Alexander Jr. 1957. *An Investigation of the Interests of Secondary School Pupils, Parents, and Teachers in Physiology.* Doctoral Dissertation. (Unpublished) Pennsylvania State University.

Heubner, Dorothy E. 1929. "A Comparative Study of the Effectiveness of Models, Charts, and Teacher's Drawings in the Teaching of Plant Structures." *School Science and Mathematics.* 29:65–70.

Hibbs, Clyde W. 1956. *An Analysis of the Development and Use of Outdoor Laboratories in Teaching Conservation in Public Schools.* Doctoral Dissertation. (Unpublished) University of Michigan.

Higgins, Conwell D. 1942. *Educability of Adolescents in Inductive Ability: An Exploratory Study in the Field of Biology at the Secondary Level.* Doctoral Dissertation. (Unpublished) New York University.

Hill, Harry A. 1930. *A Comparison Between the Biological Content of Certain Periodical Literature and the Kansas High School Course of Study.*

Master's Thesis. (Unpublished) University of Kansas. A report of this investigation appears in *Science Education*. 14:430–436.

Hollenbeck, E. Irene. 1958. *A Report of an Oregon School Camp with Program Emphasis Upon Outdoor Science Experiences.* Doctoral Dissertation. (Unpublished) University of Colorado.

Hunter, George William. 1921. "An Experiment in the Use of Three Different Methods of Teaching in the Class Room" *School Science and Mathematics*. 21:875–890. 22:20–24.

Hunter, George William. 1910. "The Methods, Content, and Purposes of Biologic Science in the Secondary Schools of the United States." *School Science and Mathematics*. 10:103–111.

Hunter, George William. 1922a. "An Attempt to Determine the Relative Value of Visual and Oral Instruction in Demonstration and Experimental Work in Elementary Biology." *School Science and Mathematics*. 22:22–29.

Hunter, George William. 1922b. "The Oral Method Versus the Laboratory Manual in the Laboratory." *School Science and Mathematics*. 22:29–32.

Hunter, George William. 1925. "The Place of Science in the Secondary School." *The School Review*. 33:453–466.

Hunter, George W., and Ahrens, H. J. Edward. 1947. "The Present Status of Science Objectives in the Secondary Schools of California." *Science Education*. 31:287–295.

Hunter, George W., and Knapp, Roy. 1932. "Science Objectives at the Junior- and Senior-High School Level" *Science Education*. 16:407–416.

Hurd, Archer Willis. 1934. "How Shall Science Instruction Be Organized?" *Science Education*. 18:106–111.

Hurd, Paul DeH. 1949. *A Critical Analysis of the Trends in Secondary School Science Teaching from 1895–1948.* Doctoral Dissertation. (Unpublished) Stanford University.

Hurd, Paul DeH. 1954a. *Science Facilities for the Modern High School.* Education Administration Monograph No. 2. Stanford University Press. Stanford, California. 52 p.

Hurd, Paul DeH. 1954b. "The Educational Concepts of Secondary School Science Teachers." *School Science and Mathematics*. 1954. 54:89–96.

Irish, E. Eugene. 1949. *A Determination of Materials Dealing with Soil Conservation and Suitable for Integration into Courses of High School Science for General Education.* Doctoral Dissertation. (Unpublished) University of Michigan.

Johnson, Keith C., and Kerwan, Thomas J. 1952. "Current Practices in the Use of Greenhouses as Part of the Biology Program in the High Schools." *Science Education*. 36:85–89.

Johnson, Palmer O. 1928. "A Comparison of the Lecture-Demonstration, Group Laboratory Experimentation, and Individual Laboratory Experimentation Methods of Teaching High School Biology." *Journal of Educational Research*. 18:103–111.

Johnson, Philip. 1956. *Science Facilities for Secondary Schools*. Misc. publication No. 17. U.S. Department of Health, Education, and Welfare. Washington, D.C. 38 p.

Johnson, Philip. 1950. *Teaching of Science in Public High Schools*. U.S. Department of Health, Education, and Welfare. Office of Education. Bulletin 1950. No. 9. Washington, D.C. 48 p.

Keeslar, Oreon. 1945. *Contributions of Instructional Films to the Teaching of High School Science*. Doctoral Dissertation. (Unpublished) University of Michigan.

Kessler, Edward. 1941. "The Readability of Selected Contemporary Books for Leisure Reading in High School Biology." *Science Education*. 25:260–264.

Kiely, Lawrence John. 1951. *An Experimental Investigation of the Effectiveness of Student-Made Drawings and Photomicrographs in Microscope Work in Pre-Professional Biology*. Doctoral Dissertation. (Unpublished) Teachers College, Columbia University. New York.

Klise, Katherine S., and Oliver, George L. 1947. "Biology—An Evaluation." *Science Education*. 31:164–171.

Knowlton, Philip A., Compiler, Committee of Publishers. 1948. *A Report to Educators on Teaching Films Survey*. Harper and Brothers. New York.

Lampkin, Richard H. 1949. *Variability in Recognizing Scientific Inquiry*. Teachers College Contributions to Education, No. 955. Teachers College, Columbia University. New York.

Laton, Anita Duncan. 1929. *The Psychology of Learning Applied to Health Education Through Biology*. Doctoral Dissertation. Contributions to Education No. 344. Teachers College, Columbia University. New York.

LeMaster, Roger A. 1952. *The Content Analysis of Selected Biology Courses of Study Compared with Content Recommended by Some Successful Biology Teachers*. Master's Thesis (Unpublished) Ball State Teachers College. Muncie, Indiana.

Leonelli, Renato E. 1947. *Principles of Physical and Biological Science Found in Eight Textbooks of General Science for Grade Eight*. Master's Thesis. (Unpublished) Boston University.

Littrell, Merritt Marshall. 1950. *A Study of Laboratory Practices and Objectives in High School Biology*. Master's Thesis (Unpublished) University of Nebraska.

Magruder, Marion V. 1936. "An Experiment in Teaching the Principle of Photosynthesis." *Science Education*. 20:146–150.

Major, Alexander Gregory. 1955. *Readability of College General Biology*

Textbooks and the Probable Effect of Readability Elements on Comprehension. Doctoral Dissertation. (Unpublished) Syracuse University.

Maller, Julius B., and Lundeen, Gerhard E. 1933. "Sources of Superstitious Beliefs." *Journal of Educational Research.* 26:321–343.

Mallinson, George G. 1949. "Materials of Consumer Science for the Junior High School." *Science Education.* 33:20–23; 138–146.

Mallinson, George G. 1952. "Some Implications for Using Films in the Teaching of Biology." *The American Biology Teacher.* 14:37–40.

Mallinson, George G., Sturm, Harold E., and Mallinson, Lois N. 1950. "The Reading Difficulty of Textbooks for High School Biology." *The American Biology Teacher.* 12:151–156.

Martin, William Edgar. 1945. "A Determination of the Principles of the Biological Sciences of Importance to General Education." *Science Education.* 29:100–105; 152–163.

Martin, William Edgar. 1952. *The Teaching of General Biology in the Public High Schools of the United States.* Bulletin 1952, No. 9. U. S. Department of Health, Education, and Welfare, Office of Education. Washington, D.C. 46 p.

McKibben, Margaret J. 1947. "The Present Status of General Objectives in the Teaching of Secondary School Biology." *Science Education.* 31:171–175.

McKibben, Margaret J. 1955. "An Analysis of Principles and Activities of Importance for General Biology Courses in High School." *Science Education.* 39:187–196.

Meier, Lois. 1927. *Health Material in Science Textbooks.* The Lincoln School of Teachers College. New York. 104 p.

Menzies, Jessie A. 1927. *An Analysis of the Generalizations and Applications in Ten College Textbooks in Biology.* Master's Thesis. (Unpublished) University of Chicago.

Merril, Amos N. 1929. "An Objective Basis for the Determination of the Objectives and Materials for a Course in Botany for Secondary Schools." *Journal of Educational Research.* 19:31–38.

Mohler, Charles W. 1950. "High School Biology and Mental Hygiene." *School Science and Mathematics.* 50:713–724.

Moyer, Harold E. 1936. *The Determination of the Relative Importance of Biological Principles as Shown by Applicatory Activities.* Master's Thesis. (Unpublished) Colorado State College of Education.

Munch, T. W. 1952. *Standards for the Construction and Equipment of Biological Science Classrooms.* Doctoral Dissertation. (Unpublished) Stanford University. Stanford, California.

Murray, C. E., Editor. 1950. *New and Improved Demonstrations, Each Il-*

lustrating a Single Scientific Principle. Master's Thesis. (Unpublished) Boston University.

Neal, Richard W. 1940. "Illustrative Material in Biology Texts." *School Science and Mathematics.* 40:267–269.

Nelson, George R. 1928. "History of the Biological Sciences in the Secondary Schools of the United States." *School Science and Mathematics.* 28:34–42; 131–144.

Newman, Earl N. 1957. *A Comparison of the Effectiveness of Three Teaching Methods in High School Biology.* Doctoral Dissertation. (Unpublished) University of Oklahoma.

Noll, Victor H. 1939. *The Teaching of Science in Elementary and Secondary Schools.* Longmans, Green and Co., Inc. New York. 238 p.

Novak, Benjamin J. 1942. "Science in the Newspaper." *Science Education.* 26:138–143.

O'Connor, Edward R. 1950. *Principles of Physical and Biological Science Found in Seven Textbooks of General Science for Grade Seven.* Master's Thesis. (Unpublished) Boston University.

Olds, Raymond C. 1936. *The Principles of Biology for Secondary Science Instruction.* Master's Thesis. (Unpublished). Colorado State College of Education.

Owens, J. Harold. 1949. *The Ability to Recognize and Apply Scientific Principles to New Situations.* Doctoral Dissertation. (Unpublished) New York University.

Peterson, Peter Victor, Jr. 1952. *A Preliminary Study of the Opportunities Presented by Fresh-Water Streams as Laboratories for Pre-College Science and Conservation Programs.* Doctoral Dissertation. (Unpublished) Cornell University.

Powers, S. R. 1926. "A Vocabulary of Scientific Terms for High School Students." *Teachers College Record.* 28:220–245.

Powers, S. R. 1925. "The Vocabularies of High School Science Textbooks." *Teachers College Record.* 26:368–392.

Pressey, Luella Cole. 1924. "The Determination of the Technical Vocabulary of the School Subjects." *School and Society.* 20:91–96.

Presson, John M. 1930. *Achievement Tests in Biology for Secondary School Use Based upon an Analysis of the Content of the Subject.* Doctoral Dissertation. (Unpublished) University of Pennsylvania.

Rabb, Donald D. 1960. *The Selection of Principles Regarded by Persons Involved in Teaching and Learning as Fundamental for Tenth Grade General Biology.* Doctoral Dissertation. (Unpublished) Pennsylvania State University. Ann Arbor, Michigan. (Dissertation Abst. 20:3667)

Relyea, Gladys. 1937. "What Are the Biology Interests of Sophomore High-School Girls." *Science Education.* 21:152–155.

Reusser, W. C. 1923. "The Status of General Biology in High Schools of the North Central States." *School Science and Mathematics.* 23:258–261.

Richards, Oscar W. 1923. "Present Content of Biology in the Secondary Schools." *School Science and Mathematics.* 23:409–414.

Richardson, John S. Editor. 1954. *School Facilities for Science Instruction.* National Science Teachers Association. National Education Association. Washington, D. C. 266 p.

Richardson, John S. 1945. "Some Problems in the Education of Science Teachers." *Science Education.* 29:249–252.

Richter, Marion. 1956. *Drawing and Learning in Biology: The Relationship Between Pupils' Drawings of Visual Aids and Their Learning in Biology.* Doctoral Dissertation. (Unpublished) Teachers College, Columbia University. New York.

Rosen, Sidney. 1955. *A History of Science Teaching in the American High School, 1820–1920.* Doctoral Dissertation. (Unpublished) Harvard University.

Rosen, Sidney. 1959. "The Origins of High School Biology." *School Science and Mathematics.* 59:473–489.

Rulon, Phillip Justin. 1933. "Sound Films versus Traditional Methods in Science Teaching." *The Nation's Schools.* 12:31–34.

Salt, E. Benton. 1936. *Health Misconceptions of Seventh-, Tenth-, and Twelfth-Grade Students.* Doctoral Dissertation. (Unpublished) New York University.

Searle, Albert H., and Ruch, Giles M. 1926. "The Study of Science Articles in Magazines." *School Science and Mathematics.* 26:389–396.

Simon, Harry Arnold. 1953. *A Basic Philosophy of Science Education and its Application in Biology Teaching.* Master's Thesis. (Unpublished) Cornell University.

Smith, Herbert A. 1949. "The Relationship Between Intelligence and the Learning Which Results from the Use of Education Sound Motion Pictures." *Journal of Educational Research.* 43:241–249.

Smith, Herbert A., and Anderson, Kenneth E. 1958. "An Inquiry into Some Possible Learning Differentials as a Result of the Use of Sound Motion Pictures in High School Biology." *Science Education.* 42:34–37.

Smith, Herbert F. 1951. *A Determination of Principles and Experiments Desirable for a Course of General Science at the Junior High School Level.* Doctoral Dissertation. (Unpublished) University of Michigan.

Smith, James R. 1952. *A Study of the Methods of Teaching Laboratory Biology in the High Schools of Delaware County.* Master's Thesis. (Unpublished) Ball State Teachers College. Muncie, Indiana.

Solomon, Marvin D., and Braunschneider, G. Edward. 1950. "Relation of Biological Science to the Social Attitudes." *Science Education.* 34:80–84.

Stafford, Wayne A. 1952. "The Textbook Versus Supplemental Material in Teaching Biology." *School Science and Mathematics.* 52:737–742.

Stathers, Allan. 1933. "The Micro-Projector Compared with the Individual Microscope in Teaching High School Biology." *Science Education.* 17:59–63.

Stiles, Glenn. 1924. "A Study of the Illustrative Material Found in Ten Biology Texts." *School Science and Mathematics.* 24:511–512.

St. Lawrence, Francis. 1951. "The Use of Teaching Aids in Biology Textbooks." *Science Education.* 35:77–81.

Stout, J. E. 1921. *The Development of High-School Curricula in the North Central States 1860 to 1918.* Supplementary Educational Monographs No. 15. University of Chicago Press. Chicago. p. 147–173.

Subarsky, Zachariah. 1948. "Human Relations in Our Time—A Challenge to The Educator." *Science Education.* 32:138–142.

Tobler, I. Vance. 1945. "Teaching Values of the Prepared Biology Drawing versus the Original Laboratory Drawing." *School Science and Mathematics.* 45:479–482.

Tyler, Ralph W. 1933. "Permanence of Learning." *Journal of Higher Education.* 4:203–204.

Tyler, Ralph W. 1930. "What High School Pupils Forget." *Educational Research Bulletin.* 9:490–492.

Tyrell, John A. Jr. 1958. *A National Survey of the Opinions of Biology Teachers as to the Most Important Areas in High School Biology and an Achievement Test in These Areas.* Doctoral Dissertation. (Unpublished) Boston University.

Urban, John. 1944. "Behavioral Changes Resulting from a Study of Communicable Diseases: An Evaluation of the Effects of Learning on Certain Actions of High School Pupils." *Teachers College Record.* 45(5):351–352.

Vinal, William Gould. 1922. "Common Mistakes in Natural History." *The Nature Study Review.* 18:329–342; 371–385.

Wallin, Russell S. 1954. *The Teaching Values of the Commercially Prepared Biology Drawings Versus the Original Detailed Laboratory Drawings.* Doctoral Dissertation. (Unpublished) Syracuse University.

Washton, Nathan S. 1951, 1952. "A Syllabus in Biology for General Education." *Science Education.* 35:84–92, 1951. 36:227–237, 1952.

Washton, Nathan S. 1941. "Findings In the Teaching of Biology." *School Science and Mathematics.* 41:553–558.

Webb, Norman, and Vinal, W. G. 1934. "Subject Matter Topics in Biology Courses of Study." *School Science and Mathematics.* 34:829–841.

Weid, Ida C. 1940. "Curriculum Relations Involved in the Conservation Program of the U.S. Biological Survey." *Science Education.* 24:260–268.

Weissman, Leah L. 1946. *Some Factors Related to the Ability to Interpret*

Data in Biological Science. Doctoral Dissertation. (Unpublished) University of Chicago.

Weltzin, Elmer M. 1933. *The Content of Biology in High School Texts.* Master's Thesis. (Unpublished) State University of Iowa. (Reported in Noll, Victor H. 1939. *The Teaching of Science in Elementary and Secondary Schools.* Michigan State College Press. East Lansing.)

Wert, James E. 1937. "Twin Examination Assumptions." *Journal of Higher Education.* 8:136–140.

Winier, Leonard Philip. 1951. *The Biological Sciences in the General Education Program at Iowa State Teachers College.* Doctoral Dissertation. (Unpublished) Teachers College, Columbia University. New York.

Wise, Harold E. 1949. "Supplementary Contributions of Sound Motion Pictures in High School Biology." *Science Education.* 33:206–213.

Wrightstone, J. Wayne. 1934. "Experimental Practices in Biology Teaching." *School Science and Mathematics.* 34:491–495.

Zim, Herbert S. 1942. "The Significance of Adolescent Interests in Biology." *The American Biology Teacher.* 4:109–112.